*Authored by Members of the*
## NON-TRADITIONAL MACHINING PROCESSES SUBDIVISION, ASTME Material Removal Division

*William W. Wood, Chairman*
Chief of Manufacturing Research and Development, LTV Vought Aeronautics Division, LTV Aerospace Corporation, Dallas, Texas

*Rufus R. C. Benton,* President-Technical Director, Chemcut Corporation, State College, Pennsylvania

*John A. Gurklis,* Ph.D., Senior Chemical Engineer, Electrochemical Engineering Division, Battelle Memorial Institute, Columbus, Ohio

*Albert E. Holm,* Chief Sales Engineer—EDM, Ingersoll Milling Machine Company, Rockford, Illinois

*Paul Rosenthal,* Head, Material Sciences Section, Applied Physics Department, Cornell Aeronautical Laboratory, Inc of Cornell University, Buffalo, New York

*Garret K. Vandenburgh,* Vice President, Anocut Engineering Company, Elk Grove Village, Illinois

*William G. Voorhes,* Chief Engineer, Elox Corporation of Michigan, Troy, Michigan
and

*Ramon E. Goforth,* Manufacturing Research Project Engineer, LTV Vought Aeronautics Division, LTV Aerospace Corporation, Dallas, Texas

*Don L. Norwood,* Senior Manufacturing Research Engineer, LTV Vought Aeronautics Division, LTV Aerospace Corporation, Dallas, Texas

*Prepared under Policy Supervision of the*
## ASTME PUBLICATIONS COMMITTEE

**1966-67**

*Joseph Seman, Chairman*
Norair Division
Northrop Corporation
Hawthorne, California

*James H. Janson*
J. H. Janson Associated Company, Inc.
Wichita, Kansas

*Thomas O. Nourie*
L. R. Nourie, Inc.
Pittsburgh, Pennsylvania

*ii*

# non-traditional machining processes

**R. K. SPRINGBORN**
Editor

*Published by the*
AMERICAN SOCIETY OF TOOL AND MANUFACTURING ENGINEERS
*Dearborn, Michigan*
1967

## NON-TRADITIONAL MACHINING PROCESSES

*Library of Congress Catalog Card Number: 67-17078*

FIRST EDITION ■ MANUFACTURING DATA SERIES

MANUFACTURED IN THE UNITED STATES OF AMERICA

# PREFACE

AJM, CHM, EBM, ECDM, ECG, ECM, EDM, IBM, LBM, PAM, USM, etc. . . .

These are the non-traditional "machining" processes . . . emerging swiftly from the laboratory and, in most cases, already implemented in production lines across the country. What are they? How do they work? How do they compare with conventional processes? What are their advantages, limitations, applications? What are their installation and operating costs? How does their future look? What is their potential for further development?

These are the questions being asked by today's designers, manufacturing engineers, plant managers, company presidents and vice presidents, and the ever-vigilant purchasing agents and cost accountants. And these are the very questions answered in the following pages.

Herewith we offer a state-of-the-art review of a new chapter in manufacturing methods — the new machining processes that make possible the impossible and more often than not do the job faster, better, and at less cost than older better-known methods. The future is here and the alert manufacturer is invited to take advantage of it where and when he can.

R. K. SPRINGBORN

Dearborn, Michigan
March, 1967

*v*

# FOREWORD

The reader will note and perhaps be startled by the consistent use of three-letter acronyms adopted herein to identify the non-traditional processes. This has been a purposeful and thoughtful choice on our part, in an attempt to bring further order into the confusion surrounding these new and sometimes misunderstood processes. The acronyms designated have been cross-checked among users of, and tool and machine manufacturers associated with, the non-traditional machining processes and, while we did not find total agreement, our selection was based on the more common and logical usage that could best serve industry now and in the years to come. In avoiding trademarks and proprietary names, we have tried to step on as few toes as possible.

Another innovation whose derivation may interest the reader is the "sketch" technique adopted in much of the artwork. This technique was selected to be in keeping with the nature of the non-traditional processes at this point in time: dynamic, still developing, largely qualitative rather than quantitative in verified data, adaptive to continual change and new uses as human imagination dictates. In other words, we have imitated the sort of sketch the engineer may doodle on his pad to illustrate a point, a process, a condition, a correlative state, or a function to one of his colleagues.

In addition to the prime authors listed on page ii, ASTME wishes to thank and give proper credit to those persons in industry and the academic setting who provided much material which the authors incorporated in their respective manuscripts. With due appreciation we cite: Guy Bellows, Senior Manufacturing Engineer, Advanced Material and Processes, Flight Propulsion Division, General Electric Company, Cincinnati, Ohio; Phillip E. Berghausen, Chief Engineer, Product Development, Electrical Machining Department, The Cincinnati Milling Machine Company, Cincinnati, Ohio; Elmer L. Boedy, Advanced Fabrication Department, Fabrication Engineering, Collins Radio Company, Cedar Rapids, Iowa; Lester V. Colwell, Professor of

Mechanical Engineering, The University of Michigan, Ann Arbor, Michigan; Jack A. Cross, Chief Engineer, Lectra-Form Division, Ex-Cell-O Corporation, Detroit, Michigan; Ward E. Duchene, Manager, Capital Equipment Division, Midvale-Heppenstall Company, Philadelphia, Pennsylvania; M. P. Ellis, Manager, Research and Development, Micromatic Hone Corporation, Subsidiary of Ex-Cell-O Corporation, Detroit, Michigan; Inyong Ham, Ph.D., Department of Industrial Engineering, Pennsylvania State University, University Park, Pennsylvania; Walter Kulischenko, Director, Industrial Products Research and Development, S. S. White Company, New York, New York; Harry C. Lorenzen, Space and Information Systems Division, Engineering Development Laboratory, North American Aviation, Inc., Downey, California; Victor E. Matulaitis, Senior Research and Development Engineer, Lectra-Form Division, Ex-Cell-O Corporation, Detroit, Michigan; John W. Meier, Chief Engineer, Industrial Products Department, Hamilton Standard Division, United Aircraft Corporation, Windsor Locks, Connecticut; John M. Morgan, Manager, Engineering and Product Development, Electrical Machining Department, Meta-Dynamics Division, The Cincinnati Milling Machine Company, Cincinnati, Ohio; Hugh H. Muller, General Manager, Chem Mill Division, Turco Products Division, Purex Corporation, Wilmington, California; Hans Nyenhuis, Vice President, Electron Beam Techniques, Inc., Plainville, Connecticut; James F. Ordway, Operations Manager, Thermal Dynamics Corporation, Lebanon, New Hampshire; Kenneth B. Steinbruegge, Research and Development Center, Westinghouse Electric Corporation, Pittsburgh, Pennsylvania; William A. Strauss, Jr., President, Chemical Micro Milling Company, Camden, New Jersey; Carl J. Weingartner, Manufacturing Engineer, AiResearch Manufacturing Company of Arizona, Phoenix, Arizona; A. T. Wheeler, Senior Research Engineer, Engineering Research Center, Western Electric Company, Princeton, New Jersey; and Arnold Wicklund, Vice President, Industrial Division, Buckbee-Mears Company, St. Paul, Minnesota.

# TABLE OF CONTENTS

*ix*

*xi*

# LIST OF TABLES

# OVERALL COMPARISON
# AND EVALUATION

Scientific and engineering advances in recent years have placed unusual demands on the metalworking industry. One aspect of these demands is that metals with high-strength-to-weight ratios have been developed to serve specific purposes. Paralleling these metallurgical developments, new methods of metal cutting and forming have emerged as a result of the search for better, faster manufacturing methods that would reduce costs and also solve the difficult fabricating problems posed by the newly-developed metals. Much of this research and development has now made the transition from the laboratory into the production setting and the new manufacturing methods are becoming standard production processes, rather than simply laboratory phenomena as they have been considered heretofore.

Those new or non-traditional processes being used in metal removal operations are the ones discussed in this book. An up-to-date, state-of-the-art review of each new process is presented to familiarize modern manufacturing and design engineers with its capabilities and current applications, as well as the pitfalls to avoid in the decision to apply a given process in a particular production situation. This chapter presents a capsule comparison and evaluation of all of the processes described in subsequent chapters with regard to: physical parameters, shape applications, materials applications, effects on machined parts, effects on process and tooling, and, ultimately, a summary of the applications, limitations, and economics of the processes.

## INTRODUCTION

The non-traditional machining processes can be classified, for ease of understanding, according to the type of fundamental machining energy they employ: (1) mechanical, (2) electro-chemical, (3) chemical, and (4) thermo-electric. These forms of energy are correlated, in Fig. 1-1, to the method of material removal, transfer media, energy source and, finally, with specific material removal processes.

It should be noted briefly that, while it serves a useful purpose, the classification of processes into mechanical, electro-chemical, chemical, etc., is arbitrary and over-simplified. Such a classification obscures the fact that *there are no material removal processes that use only one form of energy.* For example, chemical energy is extremely important in milling or turning of steel or aluminum, as is easily demonstrated by performing such an operation in a stream of nitrogen.

1

In this environment, the chips will no longer oxidize immediately upon leaving the work, but will tend to weld to the tool, increasing the cutting forces required because of the need to shear these welds to make room for further chip formation. While mechanical energy is, therefore, the primary energy in a milling (or turning) operation, chemical energy plays an important supplementary role.

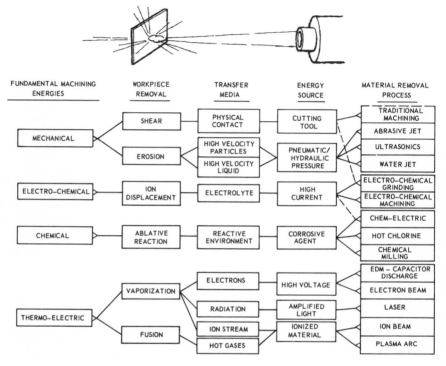

| FUNDAMENTAL MACHINING ENERGIES | WORKPIECE REMOVAL | TRANSFER MEDIA | ENERGY SOURCE | MATERIAL REMOVAL PROCESS |
|---|---|---|---|---|
| MECHANICAL | SHEAR | PHYSICAL CONTACT | CUTTING TOOL | TRADITIONAL MACHINING |
| | | | | ABRASIVE JET |
| | EROSION | HIGH VELOCITY PARTICLES | PNEUMATIC/ HYDRAULIC PRESSURE | ULTRASONICS |
| | | HIGH VELOCITY LIQUID | | WATER JET |
| ELECTRO-CHEMICAL | ION DISPLACEMENT | ELECTROLYTE | HIGH CURRENT | ELECTRO-CHEMICAL GRINDING |
| | | | | ELECTRO-CHEMICAL MACHINING |
| CHEMICAL | ABLATIVE REACTION | REACTIVE ENVIRONMENT | CORROSIVE AGENT | CHEM-ELECTRIC |
| | | | | HOT CHLORINE |
| | | | | CHEMICAL MILLING |
| THERMO-ELECTRIC | VAPORIZATION | ELECTRONS | HIGH VOLTAGE | EDM - CAPACITOR DISCHARGE |
| | | | | ELECTRON BEAM |
| | | RADIATION | AMPLIFIED LIGHT | LASER |
| | FUSION | ION STREAM | IONIZED MATERIAL | ION BEAM |
| | | HOT GASES | | PLASMA ARC |

**Fig. 1-1.** Non-traditional machining processes.

Similarly, it can be shown that mechanical energy plays a supplementary, but important, role in other non-traditional machining processes. For example, the circulation of the electrolyte in electro-chemical machining is mechanical, and is important in order to remove decomposition products from the work gap.

### Mechanical Energy

There are two types of processes that use mechanical energy: those in which material is removed principally by shear, and those in which erosion is the principal mechanism. Shear is simple machining by physical contact with a metal cutting tool and comprises all traditional machining processes; however, when material is removed by erosion, it is removed by three new, non-traditional machining processes defined as *abrasive jet, ultrasonic,* and *water jet.* The ultrasonic machining process (USM) has been in production use for approximately 17 years and represents an established means for producing small, high-precision holes and cavities. Cutting is accomplished with a tool oscillating at approximately 20,000 times per second in an abrasive slurry. Abrasive jet machining (AJM) is of more recent origin; it is currently being used in production to cut thin, hard materials that chip easily, and to cut intricate hole shapes in a broad range of materials. This process is based on the acceleration of fine abrasive particles in a high velocity gas jet through tiny nozzles. Water jet machining, which is still in the laboratory stage, utilizes a high-speed jet of liquid guided through small orifices.

### Electro-Chemical Energy

The group using electro-chemical energy represents a very important, relatively new, non-traditional machining process called *electro-chemical machining* (ECM). This process is based on a reverse electro-plating principle. Material is removed by a high-speed liquid electrolyte flowing between a cathodic tool and anodic workpiece. This process has been used in specialized production for approximately 6 years, but is indicating far greater potential application than any of the other non-traditional machining processes. As discussed below, it is perhaps the only new process that will substantially compete with traditional machining in producing a wide variety of part shapes and materials. *Electro-chemical grinding* is simply a modification of ECM in that a rotating disc is used in conjunction with the electro-chemical action. The rotating disc is abrasive and mechanically maintains a well-controlled gap between the wheel and workpiece. A relatively new variant of ECM is the *ECDM* process which combines the electric discharge with the electro-chemical principles. More complex shapes can be produced by this process through the use of a simple non-abrasive wheel.

### Chemical Energy

The third classification is the group using chemical energy and includes the chemical machining, chemical-electric, and the hot chlorine processes. These three processes are based almost entirely on a chemical action. The *chemical machining* (CHM) process is by far the most important of this group. It has been in production use for approximately 15 years and compares very favorably with traditional milling of shallow pockets in large surface sheet material. In addition, it very adequately produces thin complex metal parts that have been generally produced in the past by piercing and blanking. The CHM process is based on the principle that most metals are vulnerable to attack, i.e., erosion, by one or more chemicals; however, CHM is best suited to machining light alloys such as aluminum and magnesium. The *chemical-electric* process is essentially an electrically-assisted chemical machining process used for metal removal from alloys that are difficult to machine with acid alone. A relatively small electrical current, introduced through an acid between a tool and workpiece, will generally produce the activation necessary for adequate metal removal. The *hot chlorine process* is still in the laboratory stage.

### Thermo-Electric Energy

The last classification is the group using thermo-electric energy. It represents a very important group of machining processes based on material removal from the workpiece by means of vaporization and fusion. *Electric-discharge machining* (EDM) is a well-established process for producing holes and cavities in tough materials with high precision and has been in production use for approximately 15 years. It is, therefore, the only well-established process in the group. Metal removal is accomplished through the vaporization of the workpiece by high-frequency electrical sparks.

The principle of electron beam machining (EBM) is the transformation of the kinetic energy of high-speed electrons into thermal energy as they strike the workpiece. Laser machining (LBM) is, similarly, based on the transformation of light energy into thermal energy. *Plasma arc machining* (PAM) and *ion beam machining* (IBM) utilize an ionized plasma for energy transfer. The electron beam, laser, and plasma arc processes are being used increasingly in hole-making and slicing operations to produce small precision cuts. These three energy forms are also used to join or weld metals and alloys; however, less energy is used in joining than in machining by means of these processes because, in joining, the metal is heated only to the melting point and not to vaporization.

The *ion beam process* still remains under investigation in the laboratory.

The following sections compare the 8 most important of these non-traditional machining processes with each other and with traditional machining in order to develop a better understanding of their relative applications and limitations. The purpose is to enable the reader to more expeditiously select the correct machining process for the job to be done.

### PHYSICAL PARAMETERS OF THE PROCESSES

The important physical parameters selected for discussion are: potential, current, power, gap, and machining medium, listed in Table I-1. It is readily apparent that EBM and ECM are high-voltage/low-current, and low-voltage/high-current processes, respectively, with the remaining 6 processes falling between these two extremes. The high-voltage EBM process receives its driving energy from the ultra-high-speed electrons impinging on the part, whereas the ECM process removes block ionic particles with relatively high current. Because of the very great difference in size between ions and electrons, it will be demonstrated later that the relative removal rates between the two processes are as much as 10,000 to one in favor of ECM.

Table I-1 also makes evident that much greater power is required by the ECM process than by the others, twice as great as the next in size, PAM. In a subsequent section, it will be shown that these two processes have much higher metal removal rates than the others, although PAM has the higher with less power required because of its greater efficiency.

As illustrated in Table I-1, EDM, USM, and ECM are very close contact operations with gap distances on the order of a few thousandths of an inch. This fact makes it possible for these processes to produce very close tolerance parts, particularly USM and EDM, as will be discussed in a subsequent section; however, the close contact operation introduces electrical problems in arc-out. The gap distances in the AJM and PAM processes are intermediate in relation to EBM and LBM which can be described as having large gap distances.

### SHAPE APPLICATIONS

The capabilities of each of the 8 non-traditional machining processes with respect to part shapes to be machined are shown in Fig. 1-2. Each process has

**Table I-1. Physical Parameters of the Processes**

| Typical Parameters | Ultra-sonic | Abrasive Jet | Electro-Chemical | Chemical | Electric Discharge | Electron Beam | Laser | Plasma Arc |
|---|---|---|---|---|---|---|---|---|
| | USM | AJM | ECM | CHM | EDM | EBM | LBM | PAM |
| Potential (v.) | 220 | 110 | 10 | – | 45 | 150,000 | 4500 | 100 |
| Current (amp.) | 12 AC | 1.5 | 10,000 DC | – | 60 Pulsed DC | .001 Pulsed DC | – | 500 DC |
| Power (w.) | 2400 | 250 | 100,000 | – | 2,700 | 150 aver. 2000 peak | 2 aver. 2000 peak* | 50,000 |
| Gap (in.) | .010 | .030 | .008 | – | .001 | 4 | 6 | .300 |
| Medium | Abrasive in water | Abrasive in gas | Liquid electro-lyte | Liquid chemical | Liquid dielectric | Vacuum | Air | Argon in hydrogen |

*Based on machine capacity.

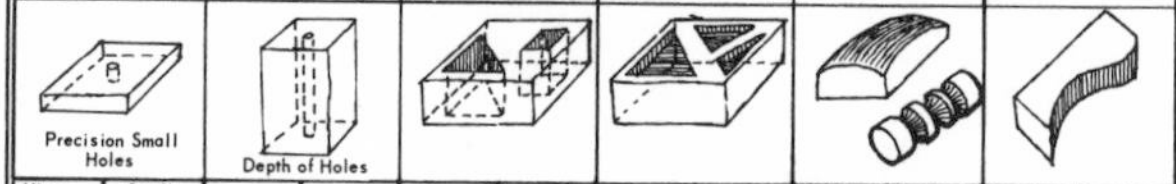

| Machining Processes | Holes | | | | Through-Cavities | | Pocketing | | Surfacing | | Through-Cutting | | Special Applications | | | |
|---|---|---|---|---|---|---|---|---|---|---|---|---|---|---|---|---|
| | Precision Small Holes | | Depth of Holes | | | | | | | | | | | | | |
| | Micro-Miniature D <.001 | Small .005 D> .001 | Shallow L/D < 20 | Deep L/D > 20 | Precision | Standard | Shallow | Deep | Double Contouring | Surfaces of Revolution | Shallow | Deep | Grinding | Honing | Deburring | Threading |
| Ultrasonic Machining (USM) | – | – | A | C | A | A | C | C | C | – | C | – | C | B | A | – |
| Abrasive Jet Machining (AJM) | – | – | B | C | C | B | – | – | – | – | A | – | A | – | A | – |
| Electro-Chemical Machining (ECM) | – | – | A | A | B | A | A | A | A | B | A | A | B | A | A | C |
| Chemical Milling (CHM) | B | B | – | – | C | B | A | C | – | – | A | – | – | – | C | – |
| Electrical Discharge Machining (EDM) | – | – | A | B | A | A | A | A | B | – | C | – | A | – | C | C |
| Electron Beam Machining (EBM) | B | A | B | C | C | C | – | – | – | – | A | B | – | – | – | – |
| Laser Machining (LBM) | A | A | B | C | C | C | – | – | – | – | A | B | – | – | – | – |
| Plasma Arc Machining (PAM) | – | – | B | – | C | C | – | – | – | C | A | A | – | – | – | C |

Legend: A = Good
B = Fair
C = Poor

**Fig. 1–2.** Shape applications of the non-traditional machining processes.

its areas of specialization among the principal shapes that can be produced by these processes: holes, through-cavities, pocketing, surfacing, through-cutting, and special applications.

## Holes

It is obvious that the EBM and LBM processes are outstanding in an application involving the production of precision small holes, defined as less than .005 in. diameter. The best processes for producing larger holes, particularly the very deep ones, are ECM and EDM. These processes can produce holes well above a length to diameter ratio (L/D) of 20, while maintaining practically no drift nor bending of the hole. When extreme accuracies are required for roundness, surface finish, or taper, conventional machining processes such as reaming and honing can be used in combination with these new electrical processes.

## Through-Cavities

Through-cavities can be produced best by USM, ECM, and EDM. Except for very small cavities, these shapes are generally machined by trepanning-type tools, which cut along the periphery, thereby leaving a core that drops out. When cutting "difficult" materials such as the super-alloys, cavities with small corner radii, or deep cavities, ECM is far superior to conventional end milling because of the deflection problems and tool breakage associated with end milling. Generally, EDM and USM are best for the more precision small cavities, while ECM is best for the larger cavities.

## Pocketing

Pocketed parts are similar to ones with through-cavities except that they have bottoms that are usually flat. This difference eliminates the use of trepanning type tools and consequently limits the non-traditional processes with regard to economic removal of material. ECM, CHM, and EDM are the principal processes for producing pockets, and they are superior to conventional processes for machining deep pockets, small corner radii, or in difficult-to-machine materials. CHM is very applicable for large surface area parts and ones requiring many small precision pockets.

### Surfacing and Through-Cutting

ECM is the major production process used to attain double contoured surfaces satisfactorily. USM, EDM, and PAM can produce these shapes to a limited extent, but generally cannot compete with ECM because of their slower removal rates. Through-cutting can be readily accomplished with the ECM, EBM, LBM, and PAM processes; however, ECM and PAM are better than the others due to their greater removal rates.

### Special Applications

Special applications are indicated in Fig. 1-2, particularly for grinding, honing, deburring, and threading by means of USM, ECM, and EDM. Although these are interesting applications, it is beyond the scope of this chapter to discuss them thoroughly.

## MATERIALS APPLICATIONS

The non-traditional machining processes have relatively good application to all metals and alloys. This is in contrast to the traditional machining processes which vary in their applicability because their capacity to machine certain classes of alloys, e.g., the super alloys, is very low. As shown in Table I-2, all metals and alloys are highly machinable by all 8 processes, with the exception of aluminum and the super alloys by means of USM, and the refractory metals and alloys by means of CHM, LBM, and PAM. In addition, it is readily apparent that USM, AJM, EBM, and LBM are very applicable processes for machining the non-metallics.

### Table I-2. Materials Applications

| Material | USM | AJM | ECM | CHM | EDM | EBM | LBM | PAM |
|---|---|---|---|---|---|---|---|---|
| *Metals and Alloys* | | | | | | | | |
| Aluminum | C | B | B | A | B | B | B | A |
| Steel | B | B | A | A | A | B | B | A |
| Super Alloys | C | A | A | B | A | B | B | A |
| Titanium | B | B | B | B | A | B | B | B |
| Refractories | A | A | B | C | A | A | C | C |
| *Non-Metals* | | | | | | | | |
| Ceramic | A | A | D | C | D | A | A | D |
| Plastic | B | B | D | C | D | B | B | C |
| Glass | A | A | D | B | D | B | B | D |

A = Good Application
B = Fair
C = Poor
D = Inapplicable

## EFFECTS ON MACHINED PART

The effects that the non-traditional machining processes have on the final machined part are the principal criteria for determining the limitations of the processes. These effects are removal rate, dimensional control, corner radii, taper, surface finish, and surface damage.

### Metal Removal Rates

As cited in Table I-3, only the ECM and PAM processes can compare with conventional machining in removal rate, this parameter being defined as the cubic inches of metal removed per hour. PAM is actually indicated in Table I-3

### Table I-3. Effects on Machined Part

| Average Effects | USM | AJM | ECM | CHM | EDM | EBM | LBM | PAM | Conventional Milling ** |
|---|---|---|---|---|---|---|---|---|---|
| Removal rates (in.³/hr.) | 1.2 | .003 | 60 | .06* | 3 | .006 | .0004 | 300 | 250 |
| Dimensional control (in.) | .0003 | .002 | .002 | .002 | .0006 | .001 | .001 | .050 | .002 |
| Corner radii (in.) | .001 | .004 | .001 | .050 | .001 | .010 | .010 | − | .002 |
| Taper (in./in.) | .005 | .005 | .001 | − | .010 | .050 | .050 | .010 | − |
| Surface finish (microinch rms.) | 10-20 | 20-50 | 5-100 | 20-100 | 10-500 | 20-100 | 20-50 | Rough | 20-200 |
| Depth of possible damage (in.) | .001 | .0001 | .0002 | .0002 | .005 | .010 | .005 | .020 | .001 |

*Penetration rate (in./hr.) is independent of surface area to be machined.
**Stagger tooth milling of 4340 Steel.

as being a faster process than conventional milling but, as illustrated in Fig. 1-2, its application to many part shapes is severely limited. ECM is approximately one-half as fast as conventional milling and, as shown in Fig. 1-2, has an extremely good application to a wide variety of part shapes. This is the primary reason that ECM is considered to have the greatest growth potential of the non-traditional machining processes. Other parameters cited in Table I-3 further enhance the future role that ECM will play in machining production parts (see Figs. 1-3, 1-4, and 1-5).

Table I-3 also shows that USM and EDM have significant removal rates when producing small, intricate, and precision parts, but are severely limited for serious consideration in producing the general run of production-type parts.

**Fig. 1-3.** Various production parts machined by ECM. *(Courtesy, LTV Vought Aeronautics Division, LTV Aerospace Corporation)*

**Fig. 1-4.** Helical-splined gears internally machined by ECM in one plunge. *(Courtesy, LTV Vought Aeronautics Division, LTV Aerospace Corporation)*

**Fig. 1-5.** Female gears, internally machined by ECM using male gears as the tools. *(Courtesy, LTV Vought Aeronautics Division, LTV Aerospace Corporation)*

EBM and LBM are so low in material removal rate that they should be considered only for special applications where no better process can produce the part.

To compare the metal removal efficiency of the various processes, removal rates (in³/hr) are plotted vs. power input (watts) in Fig. 1-6 for 8 of the processes. A significant indicator of the great differences in applicability among

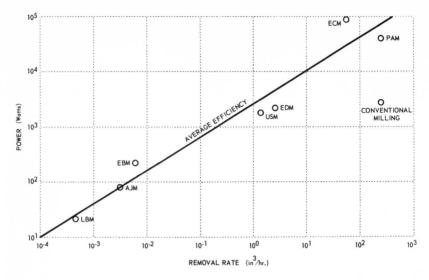

**Fig. 1–6.** Removal rate efficiency.

the processes is that removal rates vary as much as $10^6$ and power as much as $10^4$. Processes to the left of the "Average Efficiency" line are low in efficiency, while processes to the right of the line are high in efficiency. An example is ECM which, although it is a high-power/high-removal rate process, is relatively inefficient due primarily to the fact that the electrolyte heats up. This is one of the chief limitations of the process because, for proper functioning, heat removal from the electrolyte must be accomplished by external sources.

While conventional milling is shown in Fig. 1-6 to be much more efficient than any of the non-traditional machining processes in terms of power input, this cost is generally very small when compared with other costs, such as the cutting tool, tool life, removal rates, quality of part, etc.

### Dimensional Control

The dimensional control criterion in Table I-3 shows that the ECM, CHM, EBM, and LBM processes can produce parts with tolerance quality comparable to conventional milling. The USM and EDM processes, for instance, can be held to very close tolerances (.0003 and .0006 in., respectively) giving an indication of the precise dimensional tolerances that can be met by these processes. Because the PAM process cannot be controlled to close dimensions, its use is restricted to simple roughing cuts.

### Corner Radii

Corner radii is an important machining parameter for precision through-cavities such as metering orifices in control cylinders whose corner radii are often very small and must be controlled to close dimensions. These types of parts are the best applications for the USM, ECM, and EDM processes, because they can generally hold corner radii to within .001 in. Other processes are usually inadequate for such applications.

## Taper

ECM can control taper within limits because the process has no tool wear and can control the major variables. All other processes in Table I-3, excluding EBM and LBM, can be held within reasonable taper limits.

## Surface Finish

All processes can hold surface finish within acceptable limits, with the exception of PAM. USM can provide good grinding tolerances as shown by the 10 to 20 microinch rms. finish. On the other hand, EDM will produce finishes as rough as 500 microinch rms. if care is not taken with feed and other variables.

## Possible Surface Damage

Surface damage is no particular problem in the use of the non-traditional machining processes, except for the 4 thermo-electric processes (EDM, EBM, LBM, and PAM) in which damage on the machined surface is caused by the intense heat generated by the processes. Of particular concern are the damages that occur in the EDM and PAM processes, a depth on the order of .005 and .020 in., respectively. If proper precautions are not taken, such damage generally must be removed by subsequent operations, e.g., machining, sanding, or honing. The extent of the damage incurred by ECM and CHM can ordinarily be controlled by proper machining procedures.

## EFFECTS ON EQUIPMENT AND TOOLING

Another criterion for determining the relative limitations of the non-traditional machining processes is the effect that a process has on the equipment and tooling it employs. Both a qualitative and a quantitative comparison is made in Table I-4 of the typical effects that each process has on tool wear, the machining medium, the machine and equipment, safety, and toxicity.

### Table I-4. Effects on Equipment and Tooling

| Average Effects | USM | AJM | ECM | CHM | EDM | EBM | LBM | PAM |
|---|---|---|---|---|---|---|---|---|
| Tool wear ratio* | 10 | — | 0 | — | 6.6 | — | — | — |
| Machining medium** | | | | | | | | |
| Contamination | B | B | C | C | B | B | A | A |
| Heating | A | A | C | B | B | A | A | A |
| Machine and equipment | | | | | | | | |
| Maintenance | B | B | B | B | B | B | C | B |
| Protection | A | B | C | C | B | B | B | A |
| Safety | A | B | B | B | B | B | B | A |
| Toxicity | A | A | A | B | B | A | A | A |

*Tool wear ratio $= \dfrac{V_W}{V_E} = \dfrac{\text{volume of workpiece removed}}{\text{volume of electrode removed}}$

**Legend: A = No problem
B = Normal problems
C = Critical problem areas

## Tool Wear

The primary limitations of the USM and EDM processes are their relatively high tool wear ratios of 10 and 6.6, respectively. These are typical tool wear ratios for metal alloys; actual ratios will vary considerably with the type of material being machined by the USM process, e.g., from 100 for non-metallics to 1.0 for certain metals. Such high wear ratios severely limit the application of these 2 processes for 3 main reasons: (1) the cost of producing a larger number of accurate tools, (2) the time required to replace the tool, and (3) inaccuracies resulting from misalignment and worn tools. Therefore, USM and EDM should only be used for those applications in which tool wear is of no consequence.

## Machining Medium

The effects of contamination and heating on the machining medium, cited in Table I-4, indicate that ECM has critical problems in these areas, e.g., removal of contaminants and cooling of the electrolyte. Contamination arises in the form of removed ionic particles coupled with the evolution of $H_2$ gas at the electrode interface. Combined with heat generation at the interface, the result is lower conductivity and non-uniform material removal, giving lower metal removal rates and poor cutting quality. Before this process can be totally competitive with traditional machining, these problems will have to be solved.

## Machine and Equipment

Maintenance problems and problems associated with the protection of the machine and equipment are the highest in the ECM, CHM, and LBM processes. However, proper design of protection equipment will generally eliminate or minimize these problems.

## Safety and Toxicity

As indicated in Table I-4, only normal safety problems are encountered when using any of the non-traditional machining processes; in fact, in USM and PAM, there is no safety problem at all. The CHM, ECM, and EDM processes are the only ones in which there could be toxic effects on the operator or user. The remaining processes produce no toxic effects.

### SUMMARY OF APPLICATIONS AND LIMITATIONS

A qualitative summary of the relative applications and limitations of the 8 non-traditional machining processes can be derived by combining Figs. 1-2 and 1-6, and Tables I-2 and I-3. These summary evaluations, presented in Table I-5, were obtained by assigning an "A" to the most applicable processes for each criterion, and decreasing values to subsequent letters down to the least applicable.

### ECONOMIC EVALUATION

The relative economics of the non-traditional machining processes can be evaluated based on certain limitations cited in Table I-3 and Fig. 1-6, along

## Table I-5. Summary Evaluation of Applications and Limitations

| Criteria | Non-Traditional Machining Processes | | | | | | | | Traditional Machining |
|---|---|---|---|---|---|---|---|---|---|
| | USM | AJM | ECM | CHM | EDM | EBM | LBM | PAM | |
| Shape applications | C | D | A | D | B | D | D | E | C |
| Materials applications | A | A | B | B | B | A | A | B | C |
| Dimensional control and taper | A | B | B | C | A | D | D | E | B |
| Surface finish and damage | A | A | B | C | C | C | C | E | B |
| Machining medium problems | A | B | C | B | B | A | A | A | A |
| Equipment problems | A | B | C | C | B | B | C | A | A |

A = Excellent
B = Good
C = Medium
D = Fair
E = Poor

with such considerations as capital investment, tooling and fixtures, and power costs. These are listed in Table I-6 for the 8 processes discussed.

## Table I-6. Economics of Processes

| Item | USM | AJM | ECM | CHM | EDM | EBM | LBM | PAM | Traditional Machining |
|---|---|---|---|---|---|---|---|---|---|
| Capital investment | B | A | E | C | C | D | C | A | B |
| Tooling and fixtures | B | B | C | B | D | B | B | B | B |
| Power consumption | B | B | C | D* | B | B | A | A | B |
| Removal efficiency | D | D | B | C | D | E | E | A | A |
| Tool wear | C | B | A | A | D | A | A | A | B |

*Based on cost of acids

Legend:  A = Very low costs
B = Low
C = Medium
D = High
E = Very high

The capital investment costs were developed from the average price of the base machine and equipment at the time this book was published. The PAM process was given an "A" rating which represents an average price of approximately $10,000 or less for the basic equipment. The ECM process was given an "E" rating, representing an average base price of approximately $100,000 to $150,000. The remaining processes were rated accordingly between these two extremes.

Tooling and fixtures costs were based on the initial costs of the tool and the holding fixtures. Costs of replacement tools resulting from tool wear are reflected in "Tool Wear." Power consumption costs are principally electrical, with the exception of CHM where the costs are based on the chemicals used. Traditional machining is included in Table I-6 for comparison purposes.

## CURRENT EVALUATION AND STATUS

It has become apparent during the course of this chapter that the ECM process possesses the best combination of applicability and economics of the 8 non-traditional processes and compares very favorably with traditional machining. While generally speaking, traditional machining has more applicability, it is less economical to use. EDM and USM are both medium cost processes and have medium applications, thus basically limiting these processes to special applications. CHM is a medium cost process but has only fair application which limits it to the very special applications of shallow recessing large surface areas and chemical etching of small precision cavities. EBM, LBM, and PAM are neither very applicable nor economical, with the exception of PAM which is very economical. These processes will be suitable only for exceptional applications in the future.

It is evident from the figures and tables that only ECM will be in direct competition with traditional machining for the bulk of production machined parts in the foreseeable future. USM, AJM, and EDM will continue to compete for precision, unusually-shaped parts that neither ECM nor traditional processes can readily machine. As the processes become more developed, EBM and LBM will possibly compare more favorably with USM and EDM.

Fig. 1-7 illustrates the current status of the non-traditional processes with regard to the number of years they have been in research and development, and in production. USM, CHM, EDM, and PAM have been in both production and

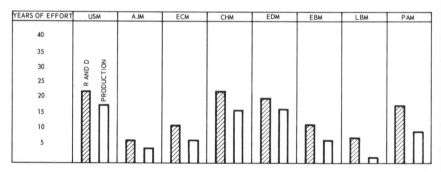

**Fig. 1-7.** Current status of non-traditional machining processes.

R and D for many years and are, consequently, relatively proven production processes. ECM and EBM have been in development an average of one-half the number of years as the first 4 named above, and are, as a result, still in the development stage in establishment of optimum parameters. The real potential of ECM, EBM, AJM, and LBM can only be determined after more development work has been accomplished.

# MECHANICAL PROCESSES

While the trend is toward the development of new material removal processes that use primarily non-mechanical energy, the two processes discussed in the following sections (abrasive jet cutting and ultrasonic machining) are important because they fill gaps that neither the conventional material removal processes nor the electro-chemical, chemical, or thermo-electric ones can properly fill. Paradoxically, these two mechanical processes find their most frequent application in the electronics industry.

Abrasive jet cutting and ultrasonic machining are both related to other processes from which they should be distinguished. For instance, there is a process variously called fluid jet cutting or jet-stream cutting, which uses a high-velocity stream of water both as the vehicle *and* as the cutting agent. This process has been demonstrated to have substantial potential for certain applications. Water jets on the order of .008 to .010 in. diameter, with velocities from 2000 to 3000 ft/sec, have been used to cut textiles, wood, and concrete. Several layers of automotive upholstery material can be cut with a continuous jet programmed to follow a desired contour. In addition, such widely divergent materials as red oak and ordinary concrete have been cut effectively. The process is not yet used commercially because suitable pumping equipment is not available. However, it does appear to have interesting potential for performing as a very thin saw to cut through materials which are either brittle (as in the case of ceramics and concrete), or tough such as wood, textiles, or plastics whose strengths are appreciably less than the strength of metals (1, 2, 3, 4, 5).

A process similar to, but distinct from, ultrasonic machining is one wherein ultrasonic vibrations are superimposed upon both conventional machine operations (such as turning, milling, and tapping) and conventional surface grinding. In all cases where sufficient amplitude was attained, cutting forces were reduced, chip formation was more uniform, and surface finish was improved (6, 7). However, these results have been obtained only under laboratory conditions and few commercial applications are known. In order to vibrate consistently, precise control must be achieved under all types of friction such as might arise within screw threads, flanged joints, etc. Consequently, each application must be engineered especially for that job. Ultrasonic assistance upon otherwise conventional machining operations probably should not be considered except as a last resort.

These two related processes are not discussed below because they have not yet been developed to the point of general commercial availability to the production engineer as machine tools or machine tool attachments. This discussion concen-

15

trates on abrasive jet cutting and on ultrasonic machining as processes for which machine tools are commercially available.

Abrasive machining would qualify as a mechanical, non-traditional material removal process. Space does not permit a discussion of the process in this chapter; however, there is comprehensive literature available on the subject (8).

## ABRASIVE JET CUTTING

Abrasive jet cutting (AJM) differs from conventional sand blasting in that the abrasive is much finer, and process parameters and cutting action are carefully controlled. AJM can be used to cut hard, brittle materials (germanium, silicon, mica, glass, and ceramics) in a large variety of cutting, deburring, and cleaning operations. The process is inherently free from chatter and vibration problems because the tool is not in contact with the workpiece. The cutting action is cool, because the carrier gas also serves as a coolant.

### Operating Principle

In AJM, material is removed from the workpiece by the impingement of fine abrasive particles entrained in a high-velocity gas stream. The following elements would be found in a typical application, shown schematically in Fig. 2-1:

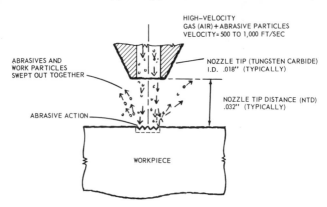

**Fig. 2–1.**   Abrasive jet cutting.

Abrasives = .001 in. in diameter
Gas (air) at a pressure of several atmospheres
Nozzle tip diameter = .003 to .018 in.
Workpiece at a distance of .032 in. from the nozzle tip
Impingement velocity = near-sonic (500 to 1000 ft/sec)

### Process Parameters

The criteria used to evaluate the process are: material removal rate, geometry of cut, surface roughness, and nozzle wear rate. Among the many variables which influence these outputs are: (1) abrasive (composition, strength, size, shape, and mass flow rate), (2) gas (composition, pressure, and velocity), and (3) nozzle (geometry, composition, distance, and inclination to work surface).

The relation of these process parameters to the output variables and their interrelation is not fully understood. A recently reported investigation on erosive wear (9) has indicated that material removal rate is a function of abrasive particle shape, in addition to size and velocity.

Theoretical models have been developed for the erosive action of abrasive particles on both brittle and ductile materials (10) and the velocity and shape of the impacting particles have been related to removal volume. For ductile materials, two types of attack have been recognized: wear due to repeated deformation, and cutting wear. Studies on gas-particle mixtures (11) have identified the mass fraction of the abrasive in the gas stream as an important parameter influencing the velocity of the mixture.

### Abrasives

Aluminum oxide is the preferred abrasive in most applications, but silicon carbide is also being used on special applications. It is important that the abrasive particles have sharp edges rather than rounded surfaces, but more specific information on the importance of these parameters is not currently available.

Particle size is important and best cutting results have been obtained if the bulk of particles vary between 15 and 40 microns (1 micron = .000039 in.). Aluminum oxide and/or silicon carbide powders of 10, 27, or 50 micron nominal diameter are available for use with the machine tool described in a later section. In addition, specific powders for cleaning, etching, abrading, and fine polishing are available for: (1) light cleaning and etching (dolomite, i.e., calcium magnesium carbonate), (2) extra fine cleaning, e.g., potentiometers (specially treated sodium bicarbonate), and (3) light, dull polishing and fine deflashing (glass beads).

Re-use of abrasive powder is not recommended, not only because its cutting or abrading action decreases but, more importantly, because contamination will clog small orifices in the cutting unit and nozzle.

All abrasive powders supplied by manufacturers can be run with clean shop air, providing that proper filters are installed in air lines. The aluminum oxide powders (10, 27, and 50 microns) and dolomite have been tested at 95 per cent relative humidity and 77°F. without filters, and no difficulty has been encountered. Sodium bicarbonate is hygroscopic in nature and filters or bottled gas must be employed when this powder is used. (Note: water is evolved in decomposition of sodium bicarbonate by means of *heat;* it is therefore advisable to avoid temperatures of 120°F. or above to prevent decomposition.)

The mass flow rate of the abrasive particles is uniquely related to gas mass flow and pressure as shown schematically in Fig. 2-2. Increasing abrasive mass flow rate will tend to increase material removal rate because more abrasive particles are at work. On the other hand, increasing the mixing ratio (i.e., the mass fraction of abrasive in the jet) lowers the sonic velocity of the stream and tends to lower material removal rate as shown in Fig. 2-3.[1] The maximum removal rate obtainable for fixed nozzle dimensions and nozzle tip distance

---

[1] The argument that, at too high a mixing ratio, the particle velocity is reduced by "interference" between particles can be ruled out because, even at a mass ratio as high as one (i.e., equal weights of abrasive and air) the volume ratio is less than 1/1000.

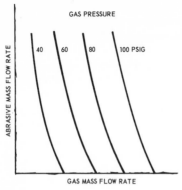

**Fig. 2-2.** Abrasive mass flow rate vs. gas mass flow rate at constant gas pressure.

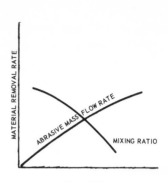

**Fig. 2-3.**

(NTD) usually lies between 2 and 20 gms/min. Typical data on the influence of mass flow rate, particle size, and abrasive composition on material removal rate are shown in Fig. 2-4.

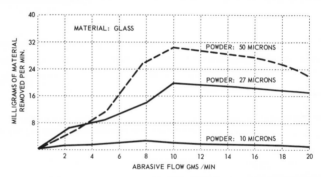

**Fig. 2-4.** How type of abrasive powder affects cutting speed in glass. *(Courtesy, S. S. White Company)*

The following cutting conditions prevail for Figs. 2-4, 2-5, and 2-7:
1) Gas carrier = air
2) Pressure at the nozzles = 75 psig.
3) Nozzle orifice (opening) = .018 in. diameter
4) Distance from work to nozzle tip (NTD) = .032 in.
5) Material = plate glass, Knoop hardness 450 to 510

## Gas

Abrasive jet cutting units are operated at pressures of 30 to 120 psi., depending on the type of work performed. Typical relationships between pressure at the nozzle and material removal rate are shown in Fig. 2-5.

The exit velocity of the gas stream has not been measured, but it is near the sonic velocity of the air-abrasive mixture. The quantities affecting flow rate

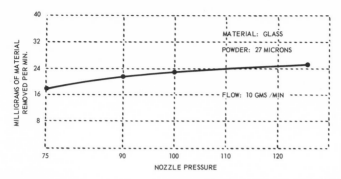

**Fig. 2–5.** How gas pressure affects cutting speed in glass. *(Courtesy, S. S. White Company)*

are: gas (molecular weight, viscosity, and sonic velocity) and particle (density and diameter). If no particles are present in the stream, elementary fluid flow theory dictates that the gas exit velocity is sonic when the pressure ratio, defined as the upstream pressure divided by the nozzle exit pressure, is more than 2. If equilibrium flow is assumed, i.e., gas velocity equals particle velocity, then the exit velocity is lower than the sonic velocity of the gas alone and the magnitude of the exit velocity decreases as the mass fraction of the abrasives in the stream increases.

### Nozzle

Nozzles are made from tungsten carbide and sapphire. For normal operation, a discharge opening with a cross-sectional area between .0001 in.$^2$ and .00036 in.$^2$ is preferred. Typical nozzle sizes and configurations are shown in Table II-1 and in Fig. 2-6.

**Table II-1. Typical Nozzle Sizes and Materials**

| Round Orifice (in.) | Material | Rectangular Orifice (in.) | Material |
|---|---|---|---|
| .007 diameter | carbide | .003 × .020 | carbide |
| .008 diameter | sapphire | .006 × .020 | carbide |
| .011 diameter | carbide | .006 × .060 | carbide |
| .018 diameter | carbide | .006 × .075 | carbide |
| .018 diameter | sapphire | .006 × .100 | carbide |
| .026 diameter | carbide | .007 × .125 | carbide |
| .026 diameter | sapphire | .010 × .030 | carbide |
| .032 diameter | carbide | .026 × .026 | carbide |

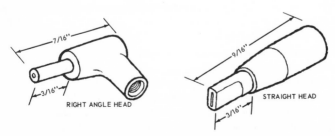

**Fig. 2–6.** Nozzle geometry. *(Courtesy, S. S. White Company)*

It is difficult to establish "average life" for the nozzle. The discard criterion will depend generally on the task for which the nozzle is being used. Nozzles made of tungsten carbide last between 12 and 30 hrs. of operation. Sapphire nozzles average approximately 300 hrs. when used with a 27 micron powder. Relative "life" between the two materials is indicated by Fig. 2-7.

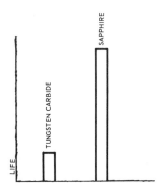

**Fig. 2-7.**

The increase in removal rate in relation to NTD (to $^9/_{32}$ in. for the conditions of Fig. 2-8) is due to acceleration of the particles after they leave the nozzle. At larger NTD ($> ^1/_2$ in. in Fig. 2-8), the expanding gas accelerates radially as well

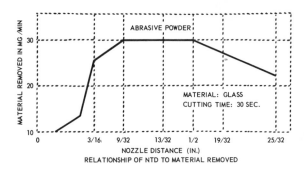

**Fig. 2-8.** How nozzle tip distance (NTD) affects cutting speed in glass. *(Courtesy, S. S. White Company)*

as axially, the geometry of stream and cut is affected, and energy is lost probably due to drag. The stream, as it emerges from the nozzle, is cylindrical for a short distance — approximately .062 in. It then diverges into a cone-shaped spray with total included angle which probably depends on pressure ratio; typically, the angle is 7 deg. as shown in Fig. 2-9.

Small holes and cuts can be made with small NTD of approximately .032 in. As the nozzle is moved away from the work, the diameter of the hole or width of the cut increases. At the same time, the walls of the cut assume an angular shape. But, even with large NTD, one wall of the cut can be kept normal to the surface plane of the work by directing the nozzle at an angle, the inclination depending on the NTD. For example, straight cuts have been produced in steel up to a depth of .06 in., and in glass to a depth of about

.25 in. Shallow cuts, only .005 in. wide, have been reported using the .003 by .060 in. nozzle.

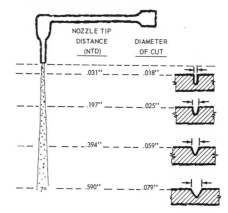

**Fig. 2–9.** Typical cutting action of .018 in. diameter nozzle. *(Courtesy, S. S. White Company)*

## Machine Tool

The cutting tool used in AJM is produced and marketed by a single manufacturer.[1] The basic machine, called "Airbrasive" Unit, is a bench unit in which the nozzle is attached to the machine by a very flexible hose and is hand held. A highly-mechanized special-purpose automatic machine has recently been introduced by the manufacturer.

An "Airbrasive" unit and several accessories are shown in Fig. 2-10. The dimensions of the cutting unit are approximately 15 by 15 by 15 in.; it operates at 110 v. AC at a power level of about 200 w. The cost of a single cutting unit is less than $1,000.

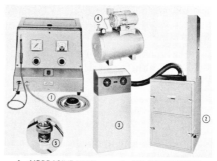

**Fig. 2–10.** "Airbrasive" unit. *(Courtesy, S. S. White Company)*

1. AIRBRASIVE UNIT    4. AIR COMPRESSOR
2. DUST COLLECTOR     5. AIR FILTER
3. EXHAUST CHAMBER

The operation of the machine can be best understood by following Fig. 2-11. When solenoid (1) is energized by closing the main switch, the system becomes pressurized. When pinch valve (2) is opened by closing the foot switch, the vibrator pulses the mixing chamber at 60 cps. This motion causes the abrasive powder in the mixing chamber to be fed through 8 small holes into an orifice

---

[1] S. S. White Company, Industrial Division, New York, New York.

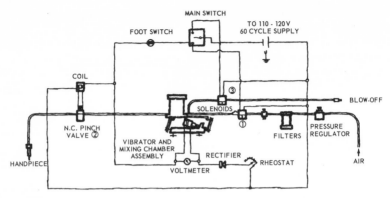

**Fig. 2–11.**   Schematic of "Airbrasive" unit. *(Courtesy, S. S. White Company)*

plate chamber. In the chamber, abrasive particles are entrained in the gas stream and discharged into a connecting hose, then into the handpiece and, finally, they emerge at high velocity from a small nozzle. The amount of powder moving through the nozzle is controlled by the amplitude of vibration which is regulated by a rheostat and indicated by the voltmeter. The air pressure in the chamber is controllable and is indicated by a meter (not shown). At the end of an operation, the system is depressurized through the blow-off valve by operation of solenoid (3).

Usually, the jet cutting units operate with an abrasive flow of 10 to 20 gms/min for cutting, and 3 to 5 gms/min for resistor trimming or other fine work. Jobs that do not require accurate positioning or precise cut can be handled by the unit described above, e.g., wire stripping, lead cleaning, deburring, deflashing, etc. For precise jobs, such as cutting threads in a glass rod, slicing precision discs in tungsten, or cutting wafers of crystalline material, modified conventional machine tools (lathe, pantograph, etc.) are used in connection with the "Airbrasive" unit.

In the unit shown in Figs. 2-10 and 2-11, the abrasive flow rate depends somewhat on the amount of abrasive in the mixing chamber. For precise operations, such as trimming thin film resistors deposited on ceramic substrates, an auxiliary feed chamber is attached to the cutting unit to provide a constant abrasive feed rate, independent of the abrasive reservoir. At flow rates of 4 gms. of abrasive per min., the machine will generally operate for 8 hours without refill.

A further refinement that can be incorporated into the unit is a drain-off solenoid which will stop abrasive flow through the nozzle in 10 to 15 milliseconds.

### Applications

**Abrading and Frosting.** AJM will uniformly abrade or frost glass, often more quickly and more economically than acid etching or grinding. An additional advantage of the process is cool, shockless cutting action by the abrasive jet. The surface roughness in this application can be varied by the grade of powder used. A 50 micron powder produces a dull finish similar to ground glass, with 38 to 55 microinch surface roughness. A 10 micron powder will produce a smooth matte finish with 6 to 8 microinch surface roughness. A 27 micron powder produces a finish somewhere between that of 50 micron and 10 micron powder. The NTD for abrading or frosting is usually from 1.0 to 3 in., with the tool held at an acute angle to the work. Designs can be reproduced clearly and accurately with abrasive jet cutting when a mask of metal or rubber is used.

**Cleaning.** Abrasive jet cutting has potential for safe removal of metallic smears on ceramics, oxides on metals, resistive coatings, etc., especially from parts too delicate to withstand manual scraping or power grinding. The position and NTD of the nozzle depends largely on the job requirements. To remove a small deposit or scribe a fine line, the nozzle should be held closer to the surface. On the other hand, many jobs are handled with the handpiece held from .5 to 3 in. away.

In electrical manufacturing, abrasive jet cutting is used to remove potting material from leads, varnish from potentiometer wires, etc.

**Resistor Adjustment.** The AJM process can precisely adjust both deposited and wire-wound resistors through accurate and controlled removal of conductive material. In addition, the process is easily automated. Cutting a contact path on a potentiometer winding, for example, is claimed to be 6 to 10 times faster with abrasive jet cutting than with any other method, leaving a cleaner, more accurate path. The width of the path desired determines the NTD. The windings, no matter how fine the wires, are unaffected. Sodium bicarbonate is the abrasive jet cutting powder usually used for this application.

**Micromodule Fabrication.** When used with micromanipulators or masks, abrasive jet cutting will change conductive paths, adjust resistance or capacitance, or shape ceramic elements. The process is precise and eliminates the danger of damage to delicate materials caused by vibration and heat.

**Semi-Conductors.** All types of operations may be performed on semi-conductor materials such as germanium, silicon, gallium, etc. Cutting, drilling, cleaning, dicing, beveling, and thinning by abrasive jet cutting are fast and accurate. Even thin, fragile sections can be processed with complete freedom from shock and heat. A high order of precision is obtainable with fixtures such as pantographs, micromanipulators, and masks.

**Crystalline Materials.** Quartz, sapphire, mica, glass, and other crystalline structures can be cut and shaped by means of AJM. Patterns can be etched using a mask or fixture.

**Steel Molds.** It is possible to make small adjustments in steel molds and dies after they have been given final hardening treatment with AJM. It is also useful for removing residual material from inaccessible parts of molds and to apply a matte finish where desired.

**Deburring.** Precision removal of fine burrs is becoming increasingly important as quality standards rise in such technologies as aerospace, medical equipment, and computers. The AJM process can remove fine burrs faster and more completely than by hand filing methods, with less dimensional loss. Moreover, the process often functions exceptionally well in hard-to-reach places, such as the intersections of drilled or tapped holes. It will also remove burrs from external and internal threads. The NTD and type of powder required by these operations are usually a matter of experimentation.

**Miscellaneous Metalworking Applications.** AJM can be used to drill and cut thin sections of hardened metal; apply numbers or trade names to parts; remove chrome, anodized finish, corrosion, or contaminants from small areas; and produce a matte finish.

**Testing Abrasion Resistance of Various Materials.** Because of the accuracy and reliability of AJM, some research laboratories are using it to test the abrasion resistance of different materials (12). Once calibrated, the cutting unit will maintain its rate of abrasive flow, etc., within close limits. Thus, comparative tests of AJM of various surfaces indicate the abrasion resistance of those surfaces.

**Miscellaneous Laboratory Applications.** Abrasive jet cutting is used in the laboratory to prepare surfaces for strain gage application, and to create artificial flaws in materials for calibration of testing equipment.

### Limitations

Abrasive jet cutting is not a fast material removal process in comparison with conventional processes. The typical 40 mg/min removal rate for plate glass is equivalent to a volume removal rate of .001 in³/min. Removal rate measurements for other materials are not available; however, lower removal rates would be expected for less hard and brittle materials. Perhaps a more meaningful way of expressing the capability of the process is to say that a .001 in³/min stock removal rate for glass corresponds to making a slot .020 in. wide by .010 in. deep by 5 in. long in one minute. This comparison emphasizes that the process has been developed for small cuts, that it has no inherent limitation on cutting speed, and that it is intended for the hard and brittle materials.

The limitations of the process for cutting either the very hard or the very soft materials have not been fully explored. The cutting of diamond by using diamond dust as the abrasive in the jet has been reported. It is believed that the softer materials, e.g., copper, are cuttable at small nozzle-work surface angles. Another, as yet unexplored, limitation of the process may be the embedding and retention of abrasives in the work materials.

The abrasion of finished surfaces by rebounding or stray abrasive particles is a further process limitation, though one readily overcome by the methods engineer. Finally, the process must be used in conjunction with a suitable dust collection system so as to protect operators and other equipment.

### Summary

A summary of the AJM process characteristics, including physical parameters, critical parameters, materials applications, part applications, and limitations, is presented in Table II-2.

### ULTRASONIC MACHINING

The development of the ultrasonic machining process (USM) was instigated largely by the more extensive use in recent years of hard, brittle materials and the necessity of finding a means to machine them effectively and efficiently. Among other difficult machining problems it has solved, USM is being used successfully to machine carbides, stainless steels, and glass. The process is best suited to machining hard and brittle materials which may be conductors or insulators.

**Table II-2. Summary of Abrasive Jet Process Characteristics**

| | *Principle* | *High-Speed Gas-Abrasive Stream* |
|---|---|---|
| Physical Parameters | *Medium*<br>Abrasive<br><br><br>Velocity<br>Pressure<br>*Nozzle*<br>Material<br>Life<br>Nozzle/Work Distance | Air, $CO_2$<br>.001 in. diameter<br>3 to 20 g/min, non-recirculating<br>$Al_2O_3$, SiC<br>500 to 1000 ft/sec<br>30 to 120 psi.<br>.003 in. to .018 in. diameter<br>Tungsten carbide, sapphire<br>12 to 300 hrs.<br>.010 to 3 in. |
| | Critical Parameters | Abrasive flow rate and velocity<br>Gas flow rate and velocity<br>Nozzle/work distance<br>Grit size and shape<br>Impact angle |
| | Materials Application | Metals and alloys (particularly<br>thin sections of hard materials,<br>e.g., germanium, silicon)<br>Non-metallics (glass, ceramics, mica) |
| | Part Applications | Drilling, cutting, deburring,<br>etching, polishing, cleaning |
| | Limitations | Low metal removal rate<br>Embedding of abrasive in workpiece<br>Taper<br>Stray cutting |

## Operating Principle

The ultrasonic machining process (also sometimes called "ultrasonic grinding" or "impact grinding") is performed by a cutting tool which oscillates at high frequency (typically 20,000 cpm. in an abrasive slurry). The tool has the same shape as the material volume to be removed from the workpiece. The high-speed reciprocations of the tool drive the abrasive grains across a small gap (a few thousandths of an inch) against the workpiece (see Fig. 2-12). The impact of the abrasive is the energy principally responsible for material removal.

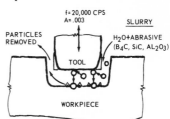

**Fig. 2-12.** Ultrasonic machining.

Early in ultrasonic machining practice, it was believed that the material was removed only by brittle failure. Therefore, it was thought that only brittle materials could be ultrasonically machined. However, it has since been observed that chips can form by this process, i.e., ductile failure can take place, and thus the range of materials that can be cut by USM is not restricted to the hard and brittle materials, though the soft and ductile materials usually can be cut more economically by other means.

## Theory

The theory that supports the ultrasonic machining process is neither complete nor uncontroversial. The following discussion is based on analyses by Shaw (13) and Miller (14) and on observations by Rozenberg, *et al.* (15).

Material removal by means of USM is believed to be due to a combination of four mechanisms: (1) hammering of abrasive particles in the work surface by the tool, (2) impact of free abrasive particles on the work surface, (3) cavitation erosion, and (4) chemical action associated with the fluid employed.

Cavitation erosion and chemical effects were initially considered to be of secondary importance by Shaw. He then assumed brittle work material failure and derived mathematical expressions for the material removal rate by means of spherical particles:

$$R_1 = k_1 \left( \frac{\pi^2 \rho a^2 d'}{6\bar{\sigma}} \right)^{3/4} f^{5/2} d^{1/4} \tag{1}$$

$$R_2 = k_1 k_2{}^{1/4} \left( \frac{4ad'}{\pi \bar{\sigma}(1 + k_3)} \right)^{3/4} f d^{-1/2} \tag{2}$$

Where:  $R_1 =$ Removal rate for impact of free particles
$R_2 =$ Removal rate for hammering by the tool
$k_1 =$ Constant
$\rho =$ Mass density of abrasive particle
$a =$ Amplitude of tool oscillation
$f =$ Frequency of oscillation
$\bar{\sigma} =$ Mean surface stress of work material at rupture
$d =$ Equivalent sphere diameter
$d' =$ Diameter corresponding to actual particle curvature at point of contact
$k_2 =$ Fraction of work area covered by abrasive
$k_3 =$ Brinell hardness of work
Brinell hardness of tool

Upon substituting values for $\rho$, $a$, $f$, $\bar{\sigma}$, and $d$, Shaw found that $R_1$ is responsible for only 20 per cent of the material removal action in coarse grinding ($d = .0012$ in.; 320 grain) and for 4 per cent of the material removal action in finish grinding ($d = .00014$; 800 grain). He concluded that hammering is the mechanism that dominates material removal in ultrasonic machining.

Upon investigating typical relations between $d'$ and $d$, he found that in first approximation:

$$R_2 \propto d \tag{3}$$

i.e., the rate of material removal due to hammering is proportional to abrasive particle diameter.

Further: $$R_2 \propto f, a^{3/4}, \sigma^{-3/4}k_2^{1/4} \tag{4}$$

Miller, in contrast to Shaw, assumed particles of cubic shape, and developed an expression for removal rate that included plastic deformation, work hardening, and chipping:

$$R = \phi(PD)(TN)(WHR)(VC)(CR)k_2 \tag{5}$$

Where:     $R$ = Volume removal rate
$\phi$ = Constant
$PD$ = Plastic deformation per blow
$TN$ = Number of blows per second
$WHR$ = Work hardening energy per unit of plastic deformation
$VC$ = Volume of material chipped per blow
$CR$ = Rate of chipping blows
$k_2$ = Fraction of tool area covered by abrasive particles, as in Shaw's formula

Miller derived a closed form expression for material removal rate; however, it includes material properties that are not readily available for polycrystalline engineering alloys, e.g., work hardening capacity and the Burgers Vector. Miller's theory apparently does not take the amplitude of oscillation into account.

Rozenberg, in a book devoted exclusively to ultrasonic machining, reviews current theories and adds observations from his own and other Russian investigations (16). He concludes that:

$$R \propto F, a^2, f^{1/2}, \bar{\sigma}^{-3/4}, k_2^{1/4} \tag{6}$$

Where:   $F$ = The static force, and the remaining symbols have the same meaning as in Shaw's formula

On the basis of high speed photography, Rozenberg also concludes that material removal is primarily due to hammer blows by the tool on abrasives in contact with the work surface. He also investigated the effect of cavitation and found that it affects the USM process in two ways: (1) by erosion of the tool, and (2) by reducing the amount of abrasive in the gap. He does not ascribe any direct influence on work material removal to cavitation erosion.

### Process Parameters

Major USM variables that control material removal rate, surface roughness, and accuracy are amplitude of tool oscillation, impact force, and abrasive size.

The influence of vibration amplitude, frequency, tool materials, abrasive, and slurry on process characteristics is discussed below. It must be pointed out, however, that not enough research has been performed to permit a comprehensive discussion of these parameters; in particular, their interrelation has not been investigated thoroughly.

**Vibration Amplitude.** As indicated in the section on "Theory," Rozenberg finds that, for a given material, removal rate is proportional to the square of the amplitude ($a$) as shown in Fig. 2-13, whereas, according to Shaw, the removal rate would vary as $(a)^{3/4}$. Pentland and Ektermanis (17) found, in exploratory

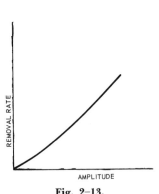

Fig. 2–13.

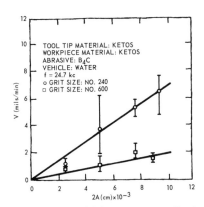

**Fig. 2–14.** Machining rate vs. amplitude of vibration for two grit sizes (14).

tests with annealed Type 4140 steel, that the square law held. Miller found a linear relation between material removal rate and amplitude for two grain sizes. His data (Fig. 2-14) have substantial scatter, however; on the other hand, they were obtained over a large range of tool amplitudes.

Goetze (19, 20) investigated the relationships among slurry concentration, frequency, tool pressure, and amplitude on hardened Type 1095 steel, and found an indication of a more complex interdependence among these parameters that should be resolved by more detailed investigation.

**Frequency.** Again there are discrepancies in reported results of mathematical predictions of the influence of frequency in the USM process. Shaw predicts that removal rate is directly proportional to the first power of frequency for a fixed amplitude (see Fig. 2-15), whereas Rozenberg observes other effects. It is

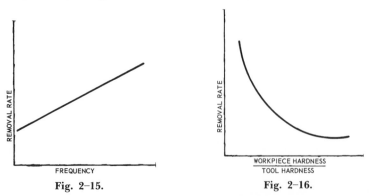

Fig. 2–15.                          Fig. 2–16.

highly probable that frequency dependence is interrelated with work and tool failure characteristics, i.e., the increase in removal rate with frequency is higher in brittle materials than in ductile materials. The frequency dependence is not very important to the process user since he cannot choose his frequency over a wide range.

**Tool Materials.** The choice of tool material is important because the cost of making the tool and the time required to change tools are critical factors in the economics of ultrasonic machining. Fig. 2-16 shows the qualitative relationship between workpiece/tool hardness vs. removal rate. An inspection of Shaw's material removal rate equation indicates that material removal rate increases with tool strength. However, he points out that if excessive tool wear is to be avoided, the static force on the transducer must be reduced as tool hardness increases. The end wear of tubular steel tools (.280 in. OD, .160 in. ID) in trepanning a ceramic material to a depth of .6 in. varied from .008 to .022 in. according to steel composition and hardness in one investigation (21). Rozenberg cites another investigation in which relative tool wear for one tool material and a variety of work materials is listed; the relative wear range was large (45 for tungsten carbide vs. 1.0 for soda glass) and the corresponding ratios of machined volume to lost tool volume were .5 and 25, respectively; the tool wear rate per unit of time was identical in both cases.

In American usage, soft steel and stainless steel are the preferred tool materials.

**Abrasive.** Boron carbide is the fastest cutting abrasive and the one most commonly used in the USM process, although aluminum oxide and silicon carbide are also employed. Boron carbide is the hardest of the three materials (1.5 times as hard as silicon carbide).

Grit or grain size has a strong influence on removal rate as illustrated in Fig. 2-17. However, when the grain size becomes comparable with tool amplitude, a maximum is reached and larger grains cut more slowly. As would be

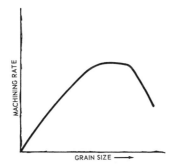

**Fig. 2–17.** Machining rate vs. grain size.

expected, the larger the grit size, the rougher the machined surface. Typical surface roughnesses resulting from grain size are:

280 grit = 25 microinch surface roughness

800 grit = 10 microinch surface roughness

In actual practice, the surface roughness obtained depends on the work material, the roughness of the tool, slurry circulation, and tool amplitude.

There is no literature on the effect of grit shape. However, it would be expected that the interrelation between the hardness of tool, grit, and workpiece affects removal rates. The number of contacts that a grit makes between the tool and workpiece also affects its shape, size, and cutting ability. Cutting rate falls off drastically when deep holes are cut, which is ascribed to grit wear and lack of replacement. Therefore, the replacement of abrasives is a cost consideration in production applications of USM similar to tool change-over.

**Slurry.** The concentration of abrasives in the slurry is an important process parameter. Ideally, the slurry brings nominal size grits to the gap, removes worn grits, and serves as a coolant. Miller (14) derived a formula for the abrasive concentration that will assure work coverage without steric hindrance, while Neppiras (22) found saturation to be between 30 and 40 per cent by volume of the abrasive/water mixture (see Fig. 2-18). Practical considerations dictate the use of lower concentrations with larger tools to insure coverage at the center.

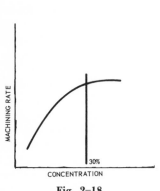

Fig. 2-18.

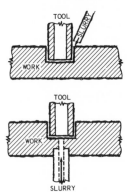

Fig. 2-19.   Modes of slurry delivery (17).

The importance of proper slurry circulation (probably coupled with its effect on particle size and shape) was demonstrated by Pentland (17) who found that, by improving slurry circulation in a drilling operation (see Fig. 2-19), material removal rates could be doubled.

Neppiras has investigated the importance of slurry viscosity and found a sharp drop-off in material removal rate with increasing viscosity. The interrelation of slurry viscosity with temperature-dependent cavitation phenomena should be considered even though no complete investigations are cited in the literature.

Water is the liquid medium used predominantly, and Neppiras has reported superior removal rates for water in comparison with those for benzene, oils, and glycerol-water mixtures. An investigation of additives that would oxidize the workpiece material appears worthwhile.

### Machine Tool

The first patent on an ultrasonic machine was granted in England in 1945. Since that time, many machines have been developed by other countries abroad, as well as in the United States. These ultrasonic machining units are supplied as cutting heads for installation in other machine tools, as bench units, and as self-contained machine tools. Fig. 2-20 shows a model of a self-contained machine tool, while Fig. 2-21 shows a similar machine in operation.

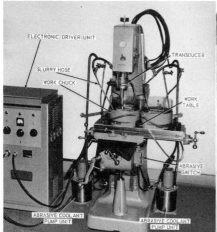

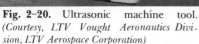

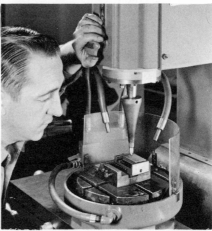

**Fig. 2–20.** Ultrasonic machine tool. *(Courtesy, LTV Vought Aeronautics Division, LTV Aerospace Corporation)*

**Fig. 2–21.** Ultrasonic machining operation. *(Courtesy, Automation and Measurement Division, The Bendix Corporation)*

The machines available today have power ratings from .06 kw. (a British ultrasonic drill) to 4 kw. (a Russian machine). American models range from .2 to 2.4 kw. The power rating (i.e., the power available as transducer input) determines the area of the tool that can be accommodated and, thereby, strongly influences the material removal rate obtainable. The obtainable down-feed rate for any given power can be maximized by reducing the tool frontal area.

The major components of an ultrasonic machining apparatus are shown schematically in Fig. 2-22. The electronic oscillator and amplifier (sometimes

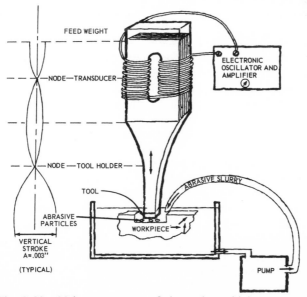

**Fig. 2–22.** Major components of ultrasonic machining apparatus.

called "generator") adjustably converts low-frequency power (60 cps.) to high-frequency power (~20,000 cps.). The transducer operates by magnetostriction; its main elements are an electromagnet and a stack of nickel plates, the length of which varies in response to the alternating field of the magnet.

The selection of the frequency and amplitude of the transducer is controlled by practical considerations. The lower limit of frequency lies at the audio-threshold (~15,000 cps.); the upper limit is imposed by the cooling requirement of the transducer, a range of 20,000 to 25,000 cps. being customary. Transducer amplitude is limited by the strength of the magnetostrictive material and is about .001 in. Both frequency and amplitude are adjustable.

The tool holder is shaped so as to amplify the motion of the transducer and, with proper design, can achieve amplitude gains of 6. Nodal and maximum amplitude locations are indicated in Fig. 2-22. In some machines, a conical connecting body is permanently fastened between the transducer and tool holder; this connecting body is made from Monel to provide maximum fatigue strength. The tool holder is threaded into the connecting body.

The tool, usually made from steel, is rigidly fastened to the tool holder by brazing or soldering. The shape of the tool corresponds to the shape to be produced in the workpiece. The direction of motion of the tool holder and tool is indicated by a double-pointed arrow in Fig. 2-22.

The workpiece is fastened to a machine base (not shown) with provision for positioning and controlled movement in 3 orthogonal axes. A feed weight maintains contact between the tool and workpiece, while the abrasive slurry is circulated by a pump.

### Tool Holder Design

The transducer, connecting body (if a part of the machine), tool holder, and tool must be in resonance to achieve useful tool amplitude and power output. Therefore the design and function of the tool holder must be understood, even though a variety of them are commercially available.

The tool holder acts as an acoustic resonance transformer which increases the velocity of the sound waves produced by magnetostriction in the transducer. To a first approximation, the effect of the work load can be neglected and simple harmonic motion can be assumed. If, further, the largest diameter of the tool holder is small compared to the wave length of the vibrations, then:

$$\frac{\partial^2 \phi}{\partial x^2} + \frac{\partial \phi}{\partial x} \frac{\partial}{\partial x} (\log A) + \frac{\omega^2}{c^2} \phi = 0 \qquad (7)$$

Where:  $x$ = Distance along axis of tool holder
$\phi$ = Velocity potential along $x$
$c$ = Velocity of sound in the tool holder
$\omega$ = Angular frequency
$A$ = Cross-section of tool holder at any point $x$.

A general solution of this equation is not available; however, it has been solved for a number of specific shapes. For example, Neppiras (23) gives the solution for the exponential taper. Here:

$$A = A_0 e^{-\gamma x} \qquad (8)$$

Where: $A_0$ = Area of the tool holder at the wide end and $\gamma$ defines the flare angle.

Upon substituting boundary conditions, he finds:

$$v = v_0 \ (\cos \omega \ x/c' - \gamma c'/2\omega \sin \omega \ x/c')e^{\gamma x/2} \tag{9}$$

Where: $v_0$ = Velocity of transducer face ($x = 0$) at resonance

$c' = \omega l/\pi$ the sound velocity in a uniform rod of length $l$

At $x = l : v = v_0 \ e^{\gamma l/2}$

The design equations for the tool holder are then:

$$l = c'\pi/\omega \ (1 - \gamma^2 c'^2/4\omega^2)^{1/2} \tag{10}$$

$$v_1/v_0 = (A_0/A_1)^{1/2} \tag{11}$$

$$v = 0 \text{ at } \tan \omega \ x/c' = 2\omega/\gamma c' \tag{12}$$

The first 2 of these equations define the length and cross-sectional area of the tool holder combinations. The third equation defines the location of nodal points, which may be important for the location of attachments.

Rozenberg (15) has tabulated formulas for area, length, and amplitude gain for a number of tool holder shapes. More recently, Vetter and Abthoff (18) have presented graphical methods for calculating exponential, cone, hyperbolic, and stepped cylindrical tool holder shapes. The method yields amplitude ratio, resonant length, contour, and planes of nodes and of maximum amplitude.

### Work Materials

As stated earlier, contrary to earlier beliefs USM can be applied to ductile materials, although it is best known for its capability to machine the hard and brittle materials which cannot be machined by conventional means. A representative ranking of process performance for various hard and brittle materials is shown in Table II-3. The data were obtained on a 700 w. machine, with a 2.5 in. diameter transducer section and a 2 in. diameter maximum recommended tool tip diameter. Note that, as in the earlier example, slow material removal rates are associated with high tool wear rates.

**Table II-3. Representative Ultrasonic Grinding Performance (13)**

| Material | Ratio of Stock Removed to Tool Wear | Maximum Practical Grinding Area (sq. in.) | Average Grinding Rate 1/2 in. Dia. Tool 1/2 in. Deep in./min. |
|---|---|---|---|
| Glass | 100/1 | 4.0 | .150 |
| Ceramic | 75/1 | 3.0 | .060 |
| Germanium | 100/1 | 3.5 | .085 |
| Tungsten carbide | 1.5/1 | 1.2 | .014 |
| Tool steel | 1/1 | 1.2 | .010 |
| Mother of pearl | 100/1 | 4.0 | .150 |
| Synthetic ruby | 2/1 | .875 | .020 |
| Carbon-graphite | 100/1 | 3.0 | .080 |
| Ferrite | 100/1 | 3.5 | .125 |
| Quartz | 50/1 | 3.0 | .065 |
| Boron-carbide | 2.5/1 | .875 | .015 |
| Glass-bonded mica | 100/1 | 3.5 | .125 |

## Geometry of Cuts

The USM process is particularly suited to:

(1) Making holes with a curved axis, non-round holes, or holes of any shape for which a master can be made, including multi-hole screens. The range of obtainable shapes can be increased by moving the workpiece during cutting.

(2) Coining operations, particularly for such easily-ultrasonically-machinable materials as glass.

(3) Threading by appropriately rotating and translating the workpiece as the tool penetrates.

The smallest holes that can be cut by USM are approximately .003 in. in diameter, hole size being limited by the strength of the tool and the clearance required for the abrasive. The largest diameter solid tool employed thus far in USM has a 3.5 in. diameter and is used with the 2.4 kw. machine. Larger holes can, of course, be cut by trepanning or rotating the workpiece.

As mentioned under the "Abrasives" and "Slurry" parameters, the depth of holes obtainable is limited by tool wear and by the difficulty encountered in feeding fresh slurry to the end of the tool. Depth/diameter ratios of 2 to 5 are possible, depending on the work material.

For accurate holes, rough and finish cuts are advisable. In general, the hole and tool tend to take the shapes shown (and exaggerated) in Fig. 2-23. Region

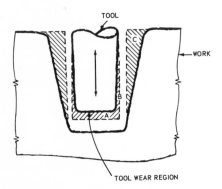

**Fig. 2–23.** Tool wear pattern.

(*a*), wear at the face of the tool, occurs because of the impact that constitutes the primary cutting action. Regions (*b*) and (*c*), taper of tool and workpiece, are caused by secondary impact of abrasives in the annular gap between tool and workpiece. Since this annulus is short at the beginning of the cut, the regions that subsequently form the annulus (near the top of the hole and the lower end of the tool) wear more and the opposing tapers result. Although the accuracies obtainable cannot be readily generalized, the reader is directed to the application examples below for specific details.

## Applications

A typical USM hole cutting operation is described below and illustrated in

Fig. 2-24. The task was to cut a .500 in. diameter hole in a .187 in. thick carbide wire drawing die.

| | Roughing Cut | Finish Cut |
|---|---|---|
| Abrasive, $B_4C$, grit size | 320 | 600 |
| Static load | 2 lbs. (20 psi.) | 2 lbs. |
| Tool diameter | .490 in. | .4992 |
| Hole diameter, top | .493 in. | .5000 ± .0002 |
| Hole diameter, bottom | .489 | .5000 ± .0002 |
| Surface roughness (microinch) | 22 | 15 |
| Time (min.) | 15 | 10 |

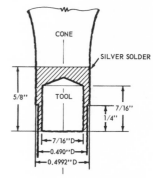

**Fig. 2–24.** Combination roughing and finishing tool for trepanning hole in tungsten carbide (14).

The production of more complex holes is illustrated in Fig. 2-25. The dimensions of the ferrite motor laminator are: OD 1.25 in., ID .625 in., .200 in. thick.

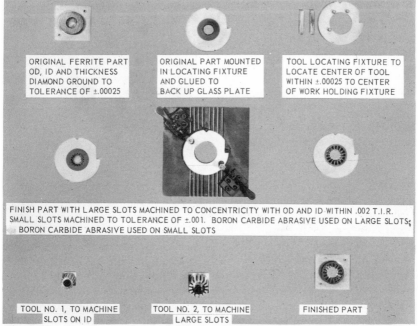

**Fig. 2–25.** Complete tooling and fixturing for the machining of motor laminators from ferrite blanks. *(Courtesy, Automation and Measurement Division, The Bendix Corporation)*

Each tool machined 16 slots simultaneously in a total machining time of 10 to 15 min.

The production of rectangular slots by USM in a phenolic impregnated ring is illustrated by Fig. 2-26. The top slot is .020 by .4 in., and extends within .01 in. of the bottom. Tolerances are ±.001 in. on size, and ±.0025 on depth. Maximum corner radius is .005 in. Machining time was 2 min.

**Fig. 2–26.** Production of rectangular slots. *(Courtesy, Automation and Measurement Division, The Bendix Corporation)*

The side slot is $\frac{1}{32}$ by $\frac{1}{4}$ in. The only critical tolerance imposed on the side slot was that the corners must be sharp. Machining time was 2 min.

A breather hole (not shown) extends up from the bottom of the 2.5 in. diameter ring. Its diameter is .013 in. and is within .001 in. of the centerline of the top slot. Machining time was "instantaneous."

Fig. 2-27 illustrates the production of 2,176 square holes in a carbon plate. Plate dimensions are 3 by 4 by .040 in.; hole dimensions are .040 by .040 in. Machining time was 10 min.

**Fig. 2–27.** Perforated carbon plate. *(Courtesy, Automation and Measurement Division, The Bendix Corporation)*

### Limitations

Like the abrasive jet cutting process, USM does not compete with conventional material removal operations on the basis of stock removal rates. It competes on the basis of shapes producible, and ability to machine hard and brittle materials. Non-metals which cannot be machined by other non-traditional processes such as EDM, are materials for which USM is particularly suitable. Nevertheless, the comparative slowness of the process in its present state of development as illustrated under "Applications," is a limitation to its usefulness.

The upper limit on total power available will probably increase through improved machine design; however, such a power increase will primarily affect the area that can be cut (volume removal rate) rather than the feed rate.

The depth of cylindrical holes producible by USM is currently limited by design of the slurry transportation system, and some improvement in this design can be expected in the future. Other limitations, for example the tendency for holes to "break out" at the bottom, are imposed by static load and amplitude; they can conceivably be overcome by programming feed force and tool amplitude.

The certain amount of trial and error required in tool design and prediction of tool wear and fracture is probably associated with the comparative newness of the process and may be likened to production engineering problems encountered some years ago in brazing by induction heating.

A summary of USM machining characteristics, capabilities, applications, and limitations, is presented in Table II-4.

**Table II-4. Summary of Ultrasonic Machining Characteristics**

| Principle | Oscillating Tool in Water-Abrasive Slurry |
|---|---|
| Physical Parameters | |
| Abrasive | $B_4C$, $Al_2O_3$, SiC |
| | 100 to 800 grit size |
| Vibration | |
| frequency | 15,000 to 30,000 cps. |
| amplitude | .001 to .004 in. |
| Tool | |
| material | soft tool steel |
| stock removal | $\{$ WC = 1.5 in. |
| tool wear | $\{$ Glass = 100 in. |
| gap | .001 to .004 in. |
| Critical Parameters | Frequency |
| | Amplitude |
| | Tool holder shape |
| | Grit size |
| | Hole depth |
| | Circulation |
| | Slurry viscosity |
| Materials Application | Metals and alloys (particularly hard metals) |
| | Non-metallics |
| Part Applications | Round and irregular holes |
| Limitations | Low metal removal rate |
| | Tool wear |
| | Hole depth |

**REFERENCES**

1. W. T. Boyd, "Mining and Transporting Coal Underground by Hydraulic Methods: A Literature Survey," *Information Circular 7887*, U. S. Bureau of Mines, 1959.
2. Eugene L. Bryan, "High Energy Jets as a New Concept in Wood Machining," *Forest Products Journal* (August, 1963), pp. 305–12.

3. E. R. McMillan, "Hydraulic Jet Mining Shows Potential as a New Tool for Coal Men," *Mining Engineering* (June, 1959), pp. 41–5.
4. B. G. Schwacha, "Liquid Cutting of Hard Materials," *U. S. Patent No. 2,985,050*, U. S. Patent Office. Assigned to North American Aviation, Inc., May 23, 1961.
5. V. G. Yugov and A. I. Osipov, "The Use of High-Speed Water Jets in Wood Cutting and Processing," The Bureau of Translations, Department of the Secretary of State, Canada. (Translated from: *The Transactions of the Central Science Research Institute of Mechanization and Energy Requirements of the Forest Industry of U.S.S.R.*, Translation No. 149, *15*, No. 6 (1960).
6. L. V. Colwell, "The Effects of High-Frequency Vibrations in Grinding," *Transactions of the ASME, 78*, No. 4 (May, 1956), 837–47.
7. R. N. Roney and B. Giardini, "Imposed High Frequency Vibrations and Their Effect on Conventional Grinding of High Thermal Resistant Materials," *ASD Project 7–757* (1962).
8. "Abrasive Machining," *ASTME Collected Papers, 63*, Book 6 (1963).
9. J. G. A. Bitter, "A Study of Erosion Phenomena," *WEAR*, Part I, *6* (1963), 5–21.
10. G. L. Sheldon and I. Finnie, "The Mechanism of Material Removal in Erosive Cutting of Brittle Materials," *ASME Paper No. WA/Prod-8* (November 7–11, 1965).
11. G. Rudinger, "Some Effects of Finite Particle Volume on the Dynamics of Gas-Particle Mixtures," *AIAA Journal, 1217* (July, 1965).
12. A. G. Roberts, W. A. Crouse, and R. S. Pizer, "Abrasive Jet Method for Measuring Abrasion Resistance of Organic Coatings," *ASTM Bulletin No. 208* (September, 1955).
13. M. C. Shaw, "Ultrasonic Grinding," *Microtecnic, 10* (June, 1956), 257.
14. G. E. Miller, "Special Theory of Ultrasonic Machining," *Journal of Applied Physics, 28* (February, 1957), 149.
15. L. D. Rozenberg *et al.*, "Ultrasonic Cutting." Authorized translation from the Russian (New York: Consultants Bureau, 1964).
16. *Op. cit.*, p. 68.
17. W. Pentland and J. A. Ektermanis, "Improving Ultrasonic Machining Rates—Some Feasibility Studies," *Transactions of the ASME, 87*, Series B. No. 1 (February, 1965), 46.
18. T. Vetter and J. Abthoff, "Das Werkstattgerechte Bemessen von Bohrruesseln zur Ultraschallbearbeitung," ("Dimensioning of Toolholders for Ultrasonic Machining"), *VDI Zeitschrift, 108*, No. 11, Part 1 (1966), 459–62; *ibid.*, No. 12, Part 2, 512–15.
19. D. Goetze, "Effect of Vibration Amplitude, Frequency and Composition of the Abrasive Slurry on the Rate of Ultrasonic Machining in Ketos Tool Steel," *Journal of the Acoustical Society of America, 28* (1956), 1053.
20. _____ "Effect of Pressure Between Tool Tip and Workpiece on the Rate of Ultrasonic Machining in Ketos Tool Steel," *Journal of the Acoustical Society of America, 29* (1957), 426.
21. A. Nomoti, "Ultrasonic Machining by Low Power Vibration," *Journal of the Acoustical Society of America, 26* (1954), 1081.
22. E. A. Neppiras, "Report on Ultrasonic Machining," *Metalworking Production* (1956).
23. _____ "A High-Frequency Reciprocating Drill," *Journal of Scientific Instruments, 30* (1953), 72. *30* (1953), 72.

# ELECTRO-CHEMICAL METAL REMOVAL PROCESSES

Electro-chemical metal removal (ECMR) is one of the newest and potentially the most useful of the non-traditional machining processes. Although the application of electrolytic machining as a metalworking tool is new, the basic principles are not. It has been known since the work of Michael Faraday (1791–1867) that if two conductive poles are placed in a conductive electrolyte bath and energized by a direct current, metal may be deplated from the positive pole (the anode) and plated onto the negative pole (the cathode). This phenomenon has been found so accurate and repeatable that one of the most common engineering terms, the coulomb, is defined as the quantity of electricity required to electrolytically deposit .00111800 gms. of silver.

For many years, the electro-plating process has directed the attention of the metalworking industry to the cathodic side of the electrolytic cell. And, until recently, the anodic side has been largely ignored. However, the explosive growth of ECMR as a metalworking tool in the last few years has been due to several factors, the most important of which are: (1) the need to machine harder and tougher materials, (2) the increasing cost of manual labor, and (3) the need to machine configurations beyond the capability of the conventional machining processes.

The ECMR processes produce surfaces which differ from those obtained by conventional mechanical removal methods. Therefore, knowledge of the effects of the ECMR processes (i.e., electro-chemical machining (ECM), electro-chemical grinding (ECG), electro-polishing, etc.) on the mechanical and surface properties of metals[1] is important to engineers, designers, and fabricators using or planning to implement these processes.

## ELECTRO-CHEMICAL MACHINING

### Operating Principles

Electro-chemical machining (ECM) operations require:

1) A cathode tool prepared with an approximate mirror image of the configuration to be machined into the workpiece.
2) A workpiece and means to hold and locate it in close proximity to the tool.
3) A means of supplying the gap between the tool and workpiece with flowing conductive liquid (electrolyte).

---

[1] For a more detailed and comprehensive discussion of the subject than presented in this chapter, see References (1) and (2).

4) A source of DC electrical power of sufficient capacity to maintain a current density between the tool and workpiece, usually greater than 100 amps/in².

As will be evident throughout this section, many variations of the above conditions and other requirements must be met in order to achieve specific results. However, whenever these conditions are present, ECM can be performed. Conversely, without any one of these conditions, it would be impossible to perform ECM.

Fig. 3-1 shows the basic arrangement of the ECM cell and a close-up schematic of the process. Since metal is removed rapidly from the workpiece, provision must be made to feed the tool and workpiece toward each other to maintain

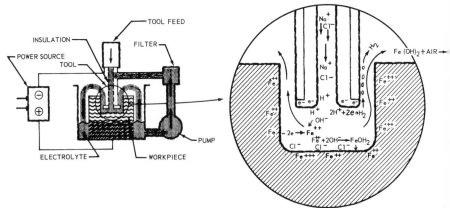

**Fig. 3–1.**   Basic electro-chemical machining cell.

**Fig. 3–2.**   Possible reactions when electrochemically machining steel with chloride electrolyte.

the end gap at a constant value. This is generally accomplished by performing ECM on a machine tool that has one or more moving members. Several types of such machines are commercially available. The direction of feed and type of moving members are established by the work to be performed and the handling characteristics of the parts. There are two types of work in which it is not necessary to feed the tool into the work:

1) Very shallow operations in which the increase in gap size can be tolerated with no loss of accuracy.

2) Operations in which the objective is simply to remove a burr or sharp edge that has been produced by a previous operation.

In these instances, machine tool requirements are greatly reduced and machining can be accomplished with relative ease.

In the electric circuit shown in Fig. 3-1, the direction of electron flow is from the workpiece and through the power supply to the tool. Since electrons will not flow through an electrolyte, the electric current is maintained by the electrons being removed from the atomic structure of the workpiece. The least strongly-bound electrons are found at the workpiece surface; these are the ones that dissociate themselves from the workpiece and flow in the electric circuit.

The metal atoms on the workpiece surface have a positive charge. Such charged atoms (ions) leave the surface because of their attraction to the negative ions that exist in the electrolyte  On the cathodic side of the cell, the electric current is completed when the electrons combine with hydrogen (H⁺) that are attracted to the surface of the tool, thus forming hydrogen gas ($2H^+ + 2e^- \rightarrow H_2$).

**Gap Control.** The flow of electric current through the gap is controlled by Ohm's Law. The equation given in Table III-1 shows that the size of the end gap is directly proportional to voltage and inversely proportional to feed rate and electrolyte resistivity. If conditions existed wherein voltage, feed rate, and

## Table III-1. ECM Principles

### Ohm's Law

(1) Current $(I) = \dfrac{\text{voltage } (V)}{\text{resistance } (R)}$

(2) Resistance $(R) = \dfrac{\text{gap length } (g) \times \text{resistivity } (\rho)}{\text{area } (A)}$

(3) Therefore: $I = \dfrac{V \times A}{\rho \times g}$

(4) Current density $(S) = \dfrac{I}{A} = \dfrac{V}{\rho \times g}$

### Faraday's First and Second Laws

(1) The amount of chemical change produced by an electric current, i.e., the amount of any substance deposited or dissolved, is proportional to the quantity of electricity passed (current × time). The amount of a material deposited $= C \times I \times t$.

(2) The amounts of different substances deposited or dissolved by the same quantity of electricity are proportional to their equivalent weights.

Theoretically the amount removed or deposited by (1 Faraday = 96,500 coulombs = 96,500 amp.-sec.) is 1 gram equivalent weight.

$$G = \frac{N}{n} \text{ (for 1 Faraday of electrical charge)}$$

### Combined Laws to Determine Removal Rates and Feed Rates

The volume of metal removed by any quantity of electricity can be calculated:

$$\text{Volume of metal} = \left[ \frac{I \times t}{96,500} \times \frac{N}{n} \times \frac{1}{d} \times \gamma \right]$$

$$\text{Specific removal rate } (s) = \left[ \frac{N}{n} \times \frac{1}{d} \times \frac{1}{96,500} \times \gamma \right] \frac{cm^3}{amp.\text{-}sec.}$$

$$\text{Feed rate } (p) = S \times s \frac{cm.}{sec.}$$

resistivity could be maintained constant throughout the gap, a perfectly uniform gap would result and absolute conformity of the form of the electrode and the workpiece would be possible. Unfortunately, it is not possible to hold the electrolyte resistivity constant because gas and heat are generated in the electrolyte as the electrolyte passes through the gap. The gas tends to increase the resistivity and the heat tends to reduce it. Sometimes the two factors offset each other to a remarkable degree; sometimes they do not. Predetermination and control of the side gap is quite difficult since it is at right angles to the feed direction and is greatly affected by the design of the tool edge.

The conditions in the machining gap are also affected by the electrical field strength. This, in turn, is affected by the shape of the electrode at any one point. Field strength and current density tend to be higher around points on the electrode. It is this phenomenon which is used in lightning rods. It is also related to what the electro-plating field calls "throwing power." This fact—that current density tends to be higher at points or sharp corners—makes it difficult to machine sharp internal corners by means of ECM.

A simple mathematical model (see Table III-1) can be made for the current and overcut conditions at any one point in the gap if resistivity, field strength, and current efficiency are assumed. The following symbols are used in Table III-1 and throughout this chapter:

| | |
|---|---|
| $A$ = Area of the current path | $n$ = Valence |
| $d$ = Density (gms/cm³) | $p$ = Electrode |
| $C$ = Constant | $R$ = Resistance |
| $E$ = Cell voltage | $\rho$ = Electrolyte resistivity |
| $G$ = Gram equivalent weight | $S$ = Current density (amp/cm²) |
| $g$ = Length of gap | $s$ = Specific removal rate |
| $\gamma$ = Current efficiency | $t$ = Time |
| $I$ = Current | $V$ = Voltage |
| $N$ = Atomic number | |

Further study of this relationship reveals a very interesting "self-adjusting" feature of ECM. If the tool advances toward the workpiece at a faster rate than the metal is removed, the gap becomes progressively smaller. As the gap becomes smaller, the current, and hence metal removal, increases proportionally (shorter path, less resistance). Therefore, the metal removal will eventually catch up with the rate of tool advance. At this point of steady gap, or equilibrium point, the equation $g = V/\rho Cp$ will be maintained. On the other hand, if the feed rate decreases, the gap will increase at first. Subsequently, the current will decrease due to increased resistance and, again, the machining rate will match the feed rate but at a different gap size. Therefore, optimum accuracy is achieved by maintaining all factors constant.

Voltage regulation is provided by highly-sophisticated power supplies that have been developed for ECM. Moving rams and slides require the best possible machine design to reduce friction and provide constant feed rates that are free of stick-slip. Uniform resistivity of the electrolyte in the gap is maintained through control of temperature, pressure, concentration, and many other factors. Space does not permit a complete discussion of the hydrodynamic conditions in the gap. However, it must always be remembered that gap size is greatly influenced by resistivity. Any flow disturbance as the electrolyte progresses through the gap will affect the gap resistivity and thus change the size of the workpiece produced. Electrolyte temperature and the amount of generated gas in the electrolyte also affect electrolyte resistivity. It is primarily the responsibility of the tool designer to control the electrolyte flow which will, in turn, maintain the tolerances required.

**Metal Removal Rate.** Theoretical metal removal rates and electrode feed rates can be calculated. Metal removal rates are governed by Ohm's Law and by Faraday's two laws of electro-chemistry as given in Table III-1. ECM metal removal rates are conveniently expressed as volume of metal removed per second. As an example, consider iron (assuming $\gamma = 1$):

$$\text{Specific removal rate } (s) = \left[ N/n \times \frac{1}{d} \left( \frac{1}{96,500} \right) \times \gamma \right] = \frac{56}{2} \times \frac{1}{7.87} \left( \frac{1}{96500} \right)$$

$$= 3.67 \times 10^{-5} \, \frac{cm^3}{amp\text{-}sec} \tag{1}$$

$$= 1.33 \times 10^{-4} \, \frac{in^3}{amp\text{-}min} \tag{2}$$

Most other metals (tungsten, with a valence of 6, is a major exception as is magnesium due to its small atomic number) have similar dissolution rates, the range being approximately .10 to .14 $in^3/1000$ amp-min. This approximation allows for any slight error introduced by inefficiencies in machining and still provides a comfortable safety factor.

Electrode feed rate is calculated:

$$p = S \times s \, \frac{cm.}{sec.} \text{ (see Table III-1)} \tag{3}$$

Metal removal rates and electrode feed rates for alloys can be computed in a similar manner. The gram equivalent weights and valences of each element in the alloy are apportioned in the same percentages as the elements appear in the alloy.

There are often significant discrepancies when metal removal rates and electrode feed rates calculated in this manner are compared with actual experimental results from the laboratory. Sometimes the laboratory metal removal rates are actually higher than the theoretical ones. Three principal causes account for the discrepancies, described in the paragraphs below.

*Current Efficiency.* Current efficiency is the efficiency of the current in removing metal. When most metals are machined with a sodium chloride electrolyte, current efficiency seems to be very close to 100 per cent. Other electrolytes, however, produce significantly lower efficiencies in the reaction. Nitrates are common electrolytes which often have a lower current efficiency. Significantly more current is required to run a given electrode with a nitrate electrolyte than is needed for a chloride electrolyte, for example, even though all other machining parameters remain constant.

*Valence.* The exact valence at which a metal enters into the electro-chemical reaction is often not known. While many metals have only one valence, and the valence at which many others enter the reaction is often known, some rather common metals enter the reaction at multiple valences. Chromium and nickel are two examples. The exact metal removal rate cannot be calculated unless valences for these metals are assigned their correct percentages in the reaction.

*Chemical Machining.* In addition to electro-chemical machining, chemical machining can occur during the process. Electro-chemical machining continually exposes a new, clean surface to the electrolyte which is easily attacked chemically. The amount of chemical machining varies, depending upon the electrolyte used and upon the metal being machined. Some metals, such as aluminum, are rather easily attacked and, in such metals, the proportion of chemical machining can be significant. Any amount of chemical machining tends to boost the actual metal removal rate above the theoretical metal removal rate. There seems to be evidence that, when steel is machined, the actual metal removal rate with a sodium chloride electrolyte is very slightly higher than the theoretical one, probably due to a certain amount of chemical machining.

### Process Parameters

A great many parameters affect the performance of an electro-chemical machine tool and the tolerances which it produces. Of course, the final question is, what will the gap be between the electrode and the workpiece. Three gaps must be considered: the frontal gap, the side gap, and the normal gap.

The frontal gap is the gap between the electrode and the workpiece in front of the electrode. The side gap is the gap between the electrode and workpiece on the sides of the electrode, on faces which are parallel to the direction of electrode feed. The normal gap is the gap between the electrode and the workpiece at any point on the electrode surface. It is the gap normal to the electrode surface at any point.

These three gaps are generally not equal and must be considered separately. The parameters which affect the gap are numerous and it is likely that no individual parameter will be equal over the entirety of an electrode and, thus, the gap will vary over the surface of an electrode.

The parameters and their relationships to one another, as well as to the frontal, side, and normal gaps, can best be illustrated by the flow chart presented

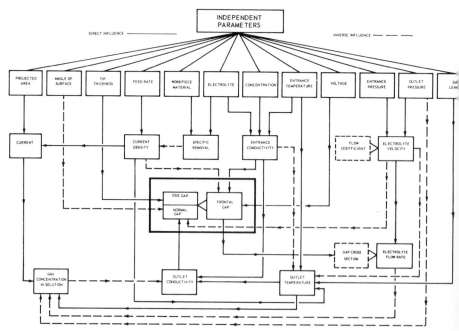

**Fig. 3–3.**   Many parameters affect the frontal, side, and normal gaps in an ECM machine. *(Industrie-Anzeiger Werkzeugmaschine und Fertigungstechnik, 8* [August 26, 1966])

in Fig. 3-3. This chart illustrates the complexity of the many parameters and their relationships to one another.

**Basic Electro-Chemical Reactions.** In an electrolyte cell, a number of chemical reactions can occur at the cathode, the anode, and in the electrolyte (see Figs. 3-1 and 3-2). Which of the possible reactions will occur is determined by the oxidation-reduction potential of the reactions. At the cathode or tool, the reaction having the smallest oxidation potential will occur. Conversely, the anode or workpiece reaction having the largest oxidation potential will occur first.

Two possible types of reactions can occur at the cathode:

1) Metal plating onto the cathode: $M^+ + e^- \rightarrow M$ ($M$ = any metal)
2) Hydrogen evolution: $2H^+ + 2e^- \rightarrow H_2$ (H = Hydrogen)

The oxidation potential of these can be varied by controlling the ECM conditions. For example, machining iron with an acid electrolyte under certain ECM conditions at low current density will result in plating metal on the cathode. However, machining iron with neutral electrolyte at high current density will not result in plating on the cathode. It is apparent that the latter operation is preferred, since the tool size must be maintained for accurate electro-machining. The major factors that influence the oxidation potential, and thus determine which of these reactions that will occur, are: (1) the metal being machined, (2) type of electrolyte, (3) current density, (4) concentration of metal ions, and (5) temperature.

Halide salts, frequently used as electrolytes, have rather simple electrolyte reactions. Three reactions can occur at the anode when a halogen electrolyte is used:

1) Metal dissolution: $M \rightarrow M^+ + e^-$
2) Oxygen evolution: $2H_2O \rightarrow O_2 + 4H^+ + 4e^-$
3) Halogen gas evolution: $2Cl^- \rightarrow Cl_2 + 2e^-$

A study of the oxidation potentials involved shows that the metal dissolution reaction is greatly favored and is really the only reaction that occurs. Tests have shown that the metal dissolution current efficiency is often on the order of 98 to 100 per cent. It would be possible, however, to establish a very undesirable set of conditions in which chlorine gas would be generated at the anode. This may be encountered, for example, when machining with a cold electrolyte (80 to 90°F.). Obviously, this must be avoided since any oxygen or halogen generation at the anode reduces the current available for metal dissolution and reduces the efficiency of the ECM process.

As pointed out earlier, when the metal ions leave the workpiece surface, a multitude of possible reactions can occur in the electrolyte. Space does not permit a thorough analysis of these possibilities. However, the following example for electro-chemical machining iron in an NaCl (sodium chloride) electrolyte is representative of the chemistry involved. As the iron ion ($Fe^{++}$) leaves the workpiece surface, it reacts with hydroxyl ions ($OH^-$) that have been attracted to the positively-charged workpiece:

$$Fe^{++} + 2(OH)^- \rightarrow Fe(OH)_2 \qquad (4)$$

The ferrous hydroxide is a green-black precipitate which, when mixed with air, oxidizes to $Fe(OH)_3$, the familiar red-brown "sludge" that is characteristic of most ECM operations.

The complete ECM operation can be represented by the following chemical equation:

$$2Fe + 4H_2O + O_2 \rightarrow 2Fe(OH)_3 + H_2 \tag{5}$$

Therefore, metal plus water plus air yields sludge and hydrogen gas. Possible reactions when machining steel with a chloride electrolyte are illustrated in Fig. 3-2.

It is interesting to note that the sodium chloride electrolyte is not used up in the ECM reactions. Neither the sodium ions nor the chlorine ions enter into the reactions. The ions in the electrolyte serve only as a vehicle to carry the electric current.

### Electrolytes and Electrolyte Handling

As shown in Fig. 3-1, the electrolyte completes the circuit between the tool and the workpiece, and permits the desired machining reactions to occur. The electrolyte also carries heat and reaction products away from the machining zone.

**Characteristics of Electrolytes.** An effective and efficient ECM electrolyte should have good electrical conductivity, be inexpensive, readily available, non-toxic and safe to use, and as non-corrosive as possible. The most widely used electrolyte at the present time is sodium chloride in water. It has the desirable characteristics outlined above, although, as with most electrolytes, its corrosiveness presents a problem. A wide range of metals have been machined successfully with sodium chloride, or sodium chloride in combination with other chemicals.

Sodium nitrate is the next most common electrolyte. It is less corrosive than sodium chloride and has other desirable characteristics, such as a relatively constant overcut and production of better surface finish in some alloys. Sodium nitrate has some undesirable characteristics including a tendency to passivate and also a lower conductivity than sodium chloride.

Other chemicals that have been used as electrolytes include potassium chloride, sodium hydroxide, sodium fluoride, sulfuric acid, and sodium chlorate.

The resistivity of an electrolyte is dependent on concentration and temperature as shown in Fig. 3-4.

**Handling of Electrolyte.** Because of the variation of resistivity with temperature and concentration, provision must be made to hold the temperature and concentration constant. Automatic temperature controls can be used to maintain temperature quite accurately, and electrolyte concentration can be maintained satisfactorily by periodic checking with a hydrometer and thermometer.

Two basic types of impurities must be removed from the electrolyte: foreign materials and the products of machining. Foreign materials include bits of steel, plastic, string, tobacco, etc. They may be introduced as impurities in the salt used for electrolyte mixing, from the operator's clothing or wiping rags, or from nearby machinery. Such particles are generally of fairly large size and can be removed by mechanical filtration.

The products of machining are generally metal oxides or hydroxides. They have an extremely small particle size (in the order of 1.0 micron) and cannot be easily filtered. Four methods are generally used to cope with them: (1) running

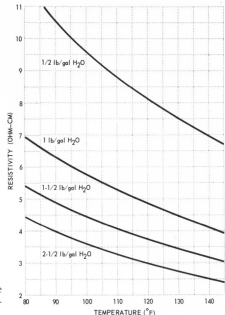

**Fig. 3–4.** Resistivity of sodium chloride solution vs. temperature and concentration.

the system until the electrolyte is too dirty to use and then dumping it (often called the run-and-dump method), (2) centrifugal separation, (3) sedimentation, and (4) the use of a clarifier.[1] The hydroxides will settle, but they settle very slowly due to their very small particle size which also makes them difficult to separate in a centrifuge.

The run-and-dump method is probably the most common. It is useful for small batches of parts and for small ECM installations. It is cumbersome on large installations and becomes economically impractical on large installations considering the cost of shutting the expensive equipment down while the electrolyte is being changed.

Centrifuges for separating the products of machining from the electrolyte are expensive to buy and to operate. They must be made entirely of stainless steel. If they leak and electrolyte enters their electrical gear or their bearings, it can cause a catastrophe. Their small size is often in their favor, however. They occupy the smallest floor space for their clarification capacity of the various methods and, thus, are desirable in installations where the cost of floor space is high.

A settling tank must be large because of the very slow settling rate of the products of machining and such tanks are usually the size of swimming pools. They work well and are relatively inexpensive to install where space is not extremely expensive. Their large size provides an excellent heat sink and eases the difficulties of good electrolyte temperature control, although it is still necessary to control the electrolyte temperature.

The clarifier, an accelerated settling system, is approximately twice the size of a centrifuge of comparable clarification capacity, and approximately one-half

---

[1] Manufactured by Anocut Engineering Company, Elk Grove Village, Illinois.

the cost. A clarifier that fits into a 7 ft. cube has a clarification rate of 24 gal/min.

A typical electrolyte cleaning system could be described as follows. The tank for storing the electrolyte is divided into a clean and dirty compartment. Electrolyte from the machine flows into the dirty tank, and is pumped from there into a centrifuge. The products of machining or sludge in the electrolyte are removed from the electrolyte by the centrifuge, and the cleaned electrolyte flows into the clean side of the tank. When required, heating or cooling of the electrolyte may be accomplished with appropriate heat exchangers in the clean side of the tank. A high-pressure pump takes electrolyte from the clean side and pumps it to the tool through a pressure reducing valve (for setting pressure), a safety filter, and flow meter. For additional flexibility in some applications, a shut-off valve and by-pass valve are used.

### Equipment, Performance, and Tolerances

An analysis of a machine tool or machining process must include an investigation of the performance and tolerance capability of that tool or process so that an accurate economic analysis may be made of its (their) application to the manufacturing facility. Neither the tolerances obtainable with ECM machines nor the factors which affect them have been widely published; however, the following discussions can be considered typical.

**Machine Tool.** The machine tool itself is one of the prime factors influencing the tolerances obtainable with ECM. Tolerances are affected by both the accuracy of movement and the rigidity of the machine tool. ECM machines are available in many different sizes and configurations, with different means for loading, set-up, tooling, alignment between work and tool, and methods for control.

A typical ECM machine (see Fig. 3-5) consists of a table for mounting the workpiece, and a platen mounted on a ram or quill for mounting the tool, inside an enclosure. The workpiece is mounted on the table, and connected in a manner ensuring good electrical contact to the positive side of the power supply.

**Fig. 3–5.** Typical vertical-type ECM machine. (*Courtesy, Cincinnati Milling Machine Company*)

The tool is mounted on the platen, with electrical connection to the negative side of the power supply. Electrolyte is pumped under pressure between the work and tool. As the tool feeds into the work with current flowing, the electrolyte carries away the machining products.

Several unique facets of ECM have necessitated developing whole new concepts in machine tools. More conventional machinery cannot cope with: the rigors of machining in a saline environment; the art of handling stainless steel; the regimen of handling extremely-high electric currents without danger to operator, part, or machine; or the construction of a drive that will move extremely slowly, yet accurately, and be free of stick-slip against high forces.

ECM machinery operates at rather substantial electrolyte pressures, commonly on the order of 200 lbs/sq in. This pressure, applied over a machining area the size of an 8.5 in. by 11 in. sheet of paper, produces a force of almost 20,000 lbs.

**Electrode.** Electrode accuracy directly affects product accuracy in ECM because the product cannot be more accurate than the electrode which produced it. The accuracy of the basic electrode form is one, but not the only, consideration. The surface finish of the electrode will also be reproduced in the surface of the machined part; therefore, poor electrode surface finish will produce a poor surface finish in the part. Part accuracy is also affected by irregularities in electrolyte flow or current flow.

The small gap between the electrode and the workpiece, discussed earlier, is called the overcut and is not necessarily uniform. Nonuniformities in the overcut can be caused by either nonuniformities in the electrolyte flow or by nonuniformities in the electric current flow between part and workpiece.

It is desirable, but not always practical, to maintain the density of electrolyte flow and the density of current flow constant. Electrolyte flow cannot always be constant because entry and exit ports to the work area must be provided for the electrolyte. In some work configurations, the flow in the immediate region of these ports will be higher than the flow in other areas.

Electric current flow should also be maintained at a constant density, if possible, so as to maintain a constant overcut. However, this is not always possible throughout all part configurations. The density of current flow through an electrolytic bath has been widely studied in connection with electroplating. Researchers have learned that current density tends to be high around points in the anode or cathode, and low around valleys. Tooling designers for ECM machinery must consider these current flow factors.

The problems of uneven density of electrolyte flow and of electric current flow can sometimes be circumvented by back-machining the electrode. Back-machining is the development of a tool from a single finished part machined by some conventional means. The electric current to the part and the electrode are reversed, so that what eventually becomes the tool is positive in the machine. The electrode is machined from the part, using the part as the cathode. The machine's electrical system is again reversed and parts are machined from this back-machined electrode.

Imperfections in the density of electrolyte flow can be caused by irregularities in the surfaces of the entry and exit ports for the electrolyte. For accurate work, these surfaces should be quite smooth. Irregularities, particularly at the entry port, will cause discontinuities in the electrolyte flow which will striate the work, resulting in fine lines parallel to the flow direction.

**Stress in the Part.** Accuracy of the finished part can be affected by distortion of the workpiece during machining caused by internal stresses in the part which are partially removed by machining. Current ECM applications include the machining of many thin forged parts. If a forging contains a great deal of internal stress, and much of the mass is cut away, then the forging will tend to distort because of the unbalanced internal stress. This same problem exists in more conventional machining processes, but not to the same degree for 2 reasons: (1) because ECM parts are often thinner than those machined conventionally and more of the mass is machined away, and (2) the internal stresses which commonly exist in parts are compressive stresses. Conventional machining also introduces compressive stresses which tend to offset the stresses removed from the part. ECM machining is stress-free and, thus, only removes stresses from the part.

**Power Supplies.** The ECM process requires low voltage DC. Voltages from 5 to 15 v. are normally used, but may go as high as 30 v. in certain cases. Currents from 100 to 20,000 amp. are being used, with even higher currents being considered for the future.

An ECM power supply must convert the AC electric power commonly available (220 or 440 v., 3-phase, 60 cycle) to the low DC voltages required. Most ECM power supplies use silicon controlled rectifiers or a saturable core reactor for voltage control. The voltage is then stepped down through a transformer and rectified by silicon rectifiers.

A good ECM power supply includes adjustable, accurate voltage controls. Means for sensing and anticipating arcs, sparks, and short-circuits must be incorporated, plus components for quickly turning off the unit when arcs or short-circuits occur.

**Accuracy.** The accuracy of the ECM process is also affected by various parameters of the process. There are, in fact, roughly a dozen factors which affect accuracy to some degree, 3 of which can be considered major: machining voltage, feed rate of the machine tool, and electrolyte temperature. A fourth, electrolyte concentration, has a gross affect on the machining gap and, thus, the tolerances; but this factor is easily controlled.

Overcut is severely responsive to machining voltage. A higher voltage produces a larger overcut and a lower voltage produces a smaller overcut (see Table III-1). The simplest way of bringing a given part to its final accurate size is by altering the machining voltage. If a trial cut indicates that the overcut should be smaller, voltage is reduced slightly and *vice versa*. Accuracy will be lost if the ECM power supply does not rigidly maintain a constant preset voltage with varying incoming line voltage and variations in total machining current. Ordinary simple rectifiers, such as those used for electroplating, vary output voltage with both of these.

The feed rate of the ECM machine must be maintained, under varying conditions of load and input voltage, or accuracy will be lost. A decrease in feed rate will increase the overcut. Conversely, an increase in the feed rate, with all other factors held constant, will decrease the overcut.

Electrolyte temperature must also be maintained constant if accurate parts are to be produced because the overcut is severely affected by electrolyte temperature. Some of the power entering into the electrolytic reaction emerges as heat in the electrolyte. This heat must be dissipated in some way so as to attain a stable condition. For example, in the machining of a rectangular hole 2.5 in. wide, 5 in. long, and 15 in. deep, failure to provide adequate electrolyte cooling can cause a 10°F. temperature rise in the electrolyte. This temperature rise is sufficient to increase the gap by .010 in., making the hole .020 in. wider at the bottom than at the top.

## Applications

**Turning.** Fig. 3-6 shows a part that can be achieved with a proper ECM installation. This small disc is 3.03 in. in diameter and is extremely thin, .006 in.

**Fig. 3–6.** Disc turned on ECM lathe to an accuracy of .0003 in. *(Courtesy, Anocut Engineering Company)*

The disc's side faces were turned on an ECM lathe. Parts of this kind have been in production for several years, and tolerances within .0003 in. have been consistently maintained.

**Die Sinking.** Fig. 3-7 is the impression for a connecting rod die. The overcut between the electrode and the part was consistently maintained throughout

**Fig. 3–7.** Die sink impression for connecting rod die machined from a solid blank in 18 min. *(Courtesy, Anocut Engineering Company)*

the surface of the part, as well as from part to part, within .002 in. Machining time for this piece was 18 min.

**Profiling and Contouring.** Another example of ECM machining is shown in Fig. 3-8, which is a cam that controls the mirror in a new, high-speed copy machine. The mirror scans the document to be copied. The cam's profile was machined by ECM and preliminary tests of the production ECM tooling used indicate a repeatable accuracy within .001 in.

ECM's capacity for unusually good repeatability is graphically illustrated by Fig. 3-9. These two stainless steel parts were machined with the same electrode.

**Fig. 3-8.** Control cam profiled by ECM after hardening, with repeatable accuracy within .001 in. *(Courtesy, Anocut Engineering Company)*

**Fig. 3-9.** Stainless steel parts electrochemically machined with same electrode (note identical reflected light patterns illustrating repeatability). *(Courtesy, Anocut Engineering Company)*

A slight dip toward the right-hand end of the parts is reflected in the light pattern. The small irregularities in this light pattern are caused by surface imperfections which must be measured in tenths, yet note that the irregularities are identical in the two parts.

**Multiple-Hole Drilling.** Fig. 3-10 shows an example of multiple-hole drilling in a stainless steel burner plate. Due to the close spacing of the 198 holes, .050

**Fig. 3-10.** Multiple hole drilling. *(Courtesy, The Ex-Cell-O Corporation)*

**Fig. 3-11.** Trepanning of nozzle valves. *(Courtesy, The Ex-Cell-O Corporation)*

in. in diameter, this part had been previously made by drilling the holes one at a time, using a tape-controlled machine. Using the cathode-tool and fixturing shown in Fig. 3-10, substantial reductions in machining time and cost were achieved. In addition, ECM eliminated the need for subsequent deburring operations on the bottom of the burner plate.

**Trepanning.** The machining of integral vanes in an Inconel X nozzle, illustrated in Fig. 3-11, was accomplished by a trepanning operation using a cathode tool insulated on the inside. With this type of machining, the raised vanes were produced inside the cathode tool with an accuracy of ±.003 in. ECM is exceptionally suited for operations of this type, since the workpiece materials are usually high-strength alloys that are difficult to machine with chip-making equipment, but are handled readily by ECM.

**Broaching.** The production of burr-free slots in a tool steel part to an accuracy of ±.001 in. by an electro-broaching technique is illustrated in Fig. 3-12.

**Fig. 3-12.** Electro-broaching slots in a tool steel part. *(Courtesy, The Ex-Cell-O Corporation)*

The cathode tool and the machined part are shown together. The electro-broaching operation effected a 75 per cent reduction in machining time over mechanical slotting.

**Steel Mill Applications.** ECM equipment is currently used by the steel industry in three areas: test cutting, sawing, and contour machining. Except for cutting tensile and impact test specimens from coupons, the machines are large and open to accommodate large pieces. Rectifiers range from 3,000 to 20,000 amp. The electrolyte used is approximately 2 lbs. of NaCl per gallon of water. Clarifying systems are sized extra large because volume metal removal and heavy cutting use the maximum output of the rectifier for long periods.

*Test Cutting.* Multiple-purpose machines with vertical and horizontal travel to accommodate the largest dimensions are used to extract test blocks from forgings, castings, and rolled shapes. The size of the test block varies, but averages 6 in³. These blocks are extracted from the work with a U-shaped copper electrode having the same dimensions as the block desired, at rates between .200 and .250 in/min.

Test blocks produced by ECM or conventional methods are further machined by ECM into tensile or impact bars. A round tensile bar within .015 in. of final size is trepanned from a test block at the rate of .200 in/min using 800 amp. Square impact bars within .015 in. of final size are trepanned from test blocks at .250 in/min using 650 amp. Six tensile or impact bars can be machined simultaneously. An electrode will cut between 15 and 20 bars before it must be replaced or repaired. The bars are then machined or ground to final size by conventional methods. Carbon, alloy, or stainless steels, irrespective of heat treatment, are trepanned at the same rates.

*Sawing.* Large ECM cut-off machines can make cuts in ingots up to 5 ft. in diameter. The travel of the electrode is vertical, and there is no horizontal or reciprocating movement of the electrode. Cuts are made up to .250 in/min using 500 to 550 amp/in of length of cut. The rate is reduced to .090 to .150 in/min when cutting high-temperature alloys because of their high resistance to electrical conductivity. When an ingot, bloom, or billet is cut for an etch test, a double electrode is used which makes 2 cuts simultaneously, parting off an etch disc with one pass. Electrodes are less expensive than comparable hack saw blades and average 2 to 4 cuts.

*Contour Machining.* ECM is also used for contour machining in forging and casting plants. The advantages are: ease of machining alloys that are difficult to cut conventionally, making multiple cuts simultaneously, making difficult contours, using one set-up to replace multiple set-ups required by conventional machining, and reduced tool costs. Metal is removed by eroding the contour, or by parting blocks or chunks from the workpiece. Typical applications are: sinking very large diameter holes, cutting interrupted threads, machining wobblers and spades on rolls, rough machining gears, sinking countersunk holes, removing defects from castings, and making odd-shaped contours.

## ELECTRO-CHEMICAL GRINDING

### Operating Principles

Electro-chemical grinding (ECG) was a precursor of ECM. This process entails the use of a grinding wheel in which an insulating abrasive is set in a conductive bonding material. DC power is connected to the part and the conductive bond of the grinding wheel in such a way that the grinding wheel is negative with respect to the part. Brushes are used on the grinder spindle to bring current into the spindle from which it then flows to the grinding wheel. A schematic of the process is illustrated in Fig. 3-13.

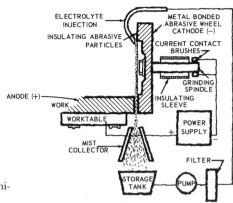

**Fig. 3-13.** Schematic of electro-chemical grinding process.

The bulk of the material is removed by electrolysis. Some of the metal is removed by the abrasive which is in contact with the work. The abrasive's principal function is to act as a spacer between the conductive bond of the grinding wheel and the part, separating the 2 and creating a small space which is filled with electrolyte. It is in this space that electrolysis actually takes place.

A DC voltage of between 4 and 8 v. is applied between the grinding wheel and the workpiece. Current densities range from approximately 800 amp/sq in. in grinding tungsten carbide to approximately 1500 amp/sq in. in grinding steels.

## Surface Finish

Surface finish produced by ECG on tungsten carbides can be expected to range from 8 to 10 microinches when plunge grinding, and 10 to 12 microinches when surface or traverse grinding. Finishes obtained on steels and various alloys will vary from 8 to 20 microinches. Generally, the higher the hardness of the alloy, the better the finish. The finishes obtained with ECG are accomplished at maximum metal removal rates and do not require a finish pass.

## Accuracy

Generally, practical tolerances using ECG are on the order of .005 in. However, accuracy to within .0005 in. with the above mentioned finishes can be obtained by making the full depth of cut in one pass. The one exception is the accuracy of sharp corners, discussed below. If higher accuracies are necessary, the majority of the stock can be removed by ECG and a final pass of .0005 to .001 in. can be taken conventionally, with the same wheel, by merely turning off the electrolytic power supply unit.

**Sharp Corners.** Inside corners cannot be ground sharper than a .010 to .015 in. radius with ECG, even though a sharp-cornered wheel is used. This characteristic of the process is due to electrolytic overcut.

## Metal Removal Rates

In general, practical metal removal rates with ECG are on the order of .004 to .030 $in.^3/min/100$ amp. However, .010 $in.^3/min/100$ amp. is often used for approximation.

## Applications

Electrolytic grinding is not really a new approach to grinding as much as it is a new *mechanism* of metal removal *using the principle of conventional grinding.* ECG is primarily electro-chemical dissolution of metal as compared to conventional grinding where metal is removed by the grit cleaving a minute chip from the workpiece. Because of these basic differences, ECG has many applications and advantages over conventional grinding as discussed briefly below.

**Carbide Cutting Tools.** Perhaps one of the most widely used applications of ECG is the grinding of carbide cutting tools. When compared with conventional grinding, ECG provides lower abrasive wheel costs and greater cutting speed. Savings of 80 per cent in wheel costs and 50 per cent in labor costs are common in grinding tungsten carbide. Other advantages include elimination of burrs, stress-free grinding, no metallurgical damage, improved surface finish, and no troublesome cracking problems because of the "cold machining" characteristic of the ECG process.

**Fragile Parts.** ECG is particularly useful in grinding fragile parts such as honeycomb (see Fig. 3-14), thin-wall tubes and skins, hypodermic needles (see Fig. 3-15), etc. In addition, high production rates can be achieved when machining the "difficult-to-machine" materials (see Fig. 3-16), regardless of whether they are hard, tough, stringy, work-hardenable, or sensitive to thermal damage.

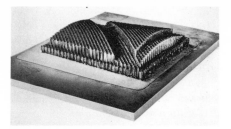

**Fig. 3-14.** Contoured stainless steel honeycomb, shaped by ECG. *(Courtesy, Anocut Engineering Company)*

**Fig. 3-15.** Hypodermic needles (left) sharpened by ECG without burrs. Needles at right were conventionally ground at same speed (note burrs). *(Courtesy, Anocut Engineering Company)*

**Fig. 3-16.** Jet engine parts electro-chemically ground faster than conventional milling with virtually no tool cost. *(Courtesy, Anocut Engineering Company)*

## ELECTRO-CHEMICAL DEBURRING

Electro-chemical deburring is a special form of electro-chemical machining which will rapidly expand in the next few years, particularly as it is applied to the mass production industries. It is an ideal method for deburring intricate parts. Intersecting holes, burrs turned up inside of bores, or burrs turned up in grooves, are excellent applications.

### Operating Principle

As in other electro-chemical processes, an electrode is made which is positioned close to the area to be machined or deburred. The electrode is negative with respect to the part, and electrolyte is passed between the two. Electrolysis removes the burrs.

### Applications

The feasibility of high-production electro-chemical deburring is being proved by an automobile manufacturer who is deburring the edges of locking grooves in the bore of connecting rods. Fig. 3-17 shows the machine built for this work which was guaranteed to deburr 720 parts per hour. Operators in preliminary tests produced up to 1080 parts per hour.

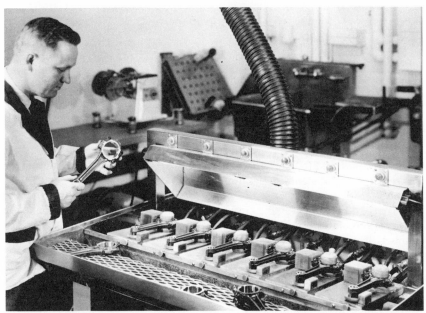

**Fig. 3–17.**   Electro-chemical deburring machine used to deburr edges of locking grooves in bore of auto connecting rods. *(Courtesy, Anocut Engineering Company)*

The deburred areas are .125 in. by .250 in. rectangular grooves which lock the bronze bearing in the connecting rod bore. These grooves are milled as part of the initial machining of the mild steel connecting rod. Burrs are thrown up around the grooves when the hole is bored to its final dimension. Fig. 3-18

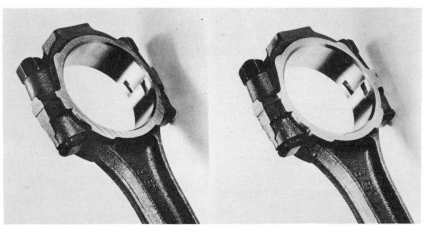

**Fig. 3–18.**   Locking grooves, shown in Fig. 3-17, before and after deburring. *(Courtesy, Anocut Engineering Company)*

shows the locking grooves before and after deburring. A slight radius is left on the edges of the grooves as the burrs are smoothly and effectively removed by electrolysis.

The removal of burrs from a broached tee slot in a forged steel automotive part (see Fig. 3-19), was accomplished in 40 sec. by ECM, as opposed to 2 min.

**Fig. 3-19.** Deburring tee-slots in automotive parts. *(Courtesy, The Ex-Cell-O Corporation)*

by hand grinding. Electro-chemical deburring reduced costs by more than 50 per cent but, more significantly, insured complete burr-removal in contrast to the random deburring that is obtained by manual methods. Electro-chemical deburring is most applicable to mass production industries where production runs are long and permit amortizing the special tooling required over a large number of parts. It lends itself particularly to production applications where burrs cannot easily be reached manually.

## ELECTRO-CHEMICAL HONING

Electro-chemical honing (ECH) combines the stock removal capabilities of ECM with the accuracy capabilities of honing. To date, the process has been adapted to ID cylindrical surfaces. However, as control techniques are improved, ECH will be used on other shapes as well.

### Operating Principle

The same basic principles described under ECM regarding current, voltage, electrolyte, and materials processed, apply to ECH. The tool is the cathode; the workpiece is the anode. The gap between the electrodes should be approximately .10 in. at the start of honing cycle and increases during the cycle. If the stock removal per cycle is great enough to result in an impractical gap, provisions are made to use an expanding cathode to keep the gap constant. A schematic of the process is illustrated in Fig. 3-20.

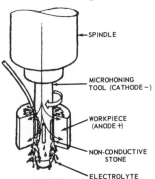

SPINDLE

MICROHONING TOOL (CATHODE –)

WORKPIECE (ANODE +)

NON-CONDUCTIVE STONE

ELECTROLYTE

**Fig. 3-20.** Schematic of electro-chemical honing.

## Tooling, Controls, Performance, and Tolerances

The tool is rotated and reciprocated through the cylinder, while the electrolyte is distributed through holes in the tool so that there is equal flow and velocity in all areas of the cylinder.

Bonded abrasive honing stones are inserted in slots in the tool. These stones are forced out radially by the wedging action of the cone in the tool. This "expansion" of the tool is controlled by an adjusting head in the spindle of the machine. The stones, which must be non-conductive, assist in the electrochemical action and generate a round, straight cylinder. They are fed out with equal pressure in all directions so that their cutting faces are in constant contact with the cylinder's surface. They abrade the residue left by the electrochemical action so that a clean surface is always presented for continuing electrolysis. If the cylinder is tapered, out-of-round, or wavy, the stones cut most aggressively on the high or tight areas and remove the geometric error.

Automatic gaging devices designed into the system initiate a signal when the cylinder is the desired diameter size, and the cycle is automatically terminated.

It the surface finish must be held to a specified roughness, the stones are allowed to cut for a few seconds after the electricity has been turned off. The characteristics of the surface finish generated in this manner is a function of the size of the abrasive grain in the stones, the relative speeds of the rotation and reciprocation motion, and the duration of the "run out" period used.

Size tolerances of .0005 in. on the diameter can be held; roundness and straightness can be held to less than .0002 in., and any surface roughness compatible with the material being cut can be duplicated on each part.

As in conventional honing, the abrasive must be self-dressing. If the stones glaze, the stock removal rate will be reduced; if they dress too rapidly, the cost of the operation will be increased. The design of the tool and the adjusting head mechanism is important for proper abrasive application.

The size of the cylinder that can be processed with ECH is limited only by the current and electrolyte that can be supplied and properly distributed in the circuit.

## MECHANICAL AND SURFACE PROPERTIES
## OF ECMR-PROCESSED METALS

The primary advantages of the ECMR processes are that they do not cause certain undesirable surface effects that can occur with conventional mechanical machining or grinding operations, and they frequently have better wear, friction, and corrosion characteristics than mechanically finished surfaces (2). Some of the desirable surface characteristics of ECMR-processed parts are illustrated by the following features of the ECM process: (1) stress-free machining, (2) burr-free machining, (3) no tool-to-workpiece contact and, therefore, no tool wear, and (4) no burning or thermal damage to workpiece surfaces.

Although these characteristics relate specifically to ECM, most of these same advantages can be attributed to electro-polishing and electro-chemical grinding (ECG), even though ECG is essentially a low- or no-stress grinding operation. Since ECG is a combination of electro-chemical (about 85 to 95 per cent) and abrasive metal removal, some residual stresses can be introduced to the metal surface, but at a greatly reduced level compared with conventional mechanical grinding. Additional advantages of the ECG process are: relative lack of surface cracks, heat checks, or fractures in ECG parts, and the capability to produce burr-free surfaces and to machine delicate workpieces such as honeycombs. Similar advantages are found in the electro-chemical honing process which also uses an abrasive assist.

### Surface Finishes

The surface finish of an ECMR part will depend on the metal or alloy being processed, the electrolyte, and the operating conditions used. The most important items are probably the choice of electrolyte, and the chemistry and microstructure of the metal or alloy being machined. Typical surface roughness data for the ECMR processes are presented in Table III-2.

### Table III-2. Typical Surface-Roughness Data for ECMR Processes

| Method | Surface-Roughness Range | |
| --- | --- | --- |
| | Overall (microinches) | Average (microinches) |
| Electro-chemical machining (ECM) | 5-150 | 10-30 |
| Electro-chemical grinding (ECG) | 3-40 | 5-20 |
| Electro-polishing | 3-50 | 3-20 |

Electro-chemical machining of nickel-base, cobalt-base, and stainless steel alloys generally produces smoother surfaces (e.g., 5 to 15 microinches) than those obtained with iron-base alloys and steels (e.g., 25 to 60 microinches).

When the ECM workpiece-electrolyte combination or operating conditions are not optimum, nonuniform dissolution of metals and alloys will occur. This is evidenced by an inability to cut the particular metal or alloy at all, or as selective etch, intergranular attack, or pitting. These latter defects adversely affect mechanical properties.

In practice, the problems of selective etch and pitting during ECM have been greatly minimized or avoided by developing electrolytes and operating conditions so as to promote uniform dissolution of the alloy. In addition, changes in the heat-treat operations, aimed at producing alloy parts with more uniform dissolution characteristics, can help minimize the problems.

### Mechanical Properties

The ECMR processes generally have a neutral effect (i.e., no significant gain or loss) on mechanical properties such as yield strength, ultimate tensile strength, sustained-load strength, ductility, hardness, etc., for most metals and alloys.

The results of an evaluation program by Krieg (3) showed that electro-chemical machining (ECM) had no harmful effects on the mechanical properties of forged SAE-4140 alloy steel. The close agreement between the tensile and ductility values of the control specimen (conventionally mechanically machined) and the ECM materials is shown in Table III-3. Krieg also showed that the values of

Table III-3. Comparison of Mechanical Properties of ECM-Processed
and Conventionally Machined (Control) 4140 Steel[a]

| Specimen Type and Number | Tensile Yield (FTY), 1000 psi. | Tensile Ultimate (FTU), 1000 psi. | Elongation, per cent | Reduction of Area, per cent |
|---|---|---|---|---|
| Control 1 | 171.0 | 177.5 | 9.5 | 38.5 |
| Control 2 | 174.5 | 184.5 | 11.0 | 33.5 |
| Control 3 | 176.0 | 185.0 | 9.5[b] | 37.0 |
| ECM 1 | 172.0 | 179.5 | 9.0 | 41.0 |
| ECM 2 | 171.0 | 180.0 | 7.5 | 32.5 |
| ECM 3 | 174.5 | 182.0 | 8.5[b] | 35.0 |

[a] Data are from Krieg (3).
[b] Specimens broke outside of middle gage length.

notched-tensile strength, notched-sensitivity, and the sustained-load characteristics for the control and ECM specimens agreed closely with one another. For
example, the average value of the notched-tensile strength was 192,500 psi. for
the contol specimens and 191,000 psi. for the ECM specimens.

Bogorad, et al. (4) showed that electro-polishing had no significant effect on
the yield strength, ultimate tensile strength, elongation or reduction-in-area of
stainless steel. Data for specimens electro-polished in the annealed and quenched
conditions are given in Table III-4.

Table III-4. Effect of Electro-Polishing on the Mechanical Properties
of Stainless Steel[a]

| Surface Treatment | Yield Strength, 1000 psi. | Ultimate Tensile Strength, 1000 psi. | Elongation, per cent | Reduction of Area, per cent |
|---|---|---|---|---|
| Ground after annealing | 34.2 | 73.0 | 36.1 | 74.8 |
| Electro-polished after grinding and annealing | 35.0 | 71.5 | 35.7 | 78.9 |
| Ground after quenching | 82.4 | 104.2 | 18.4 | 69.9 |
| Electro-polished after grinding and quenching | 81.1 | 104.0 | 17.7 | 68.9 |

[a] Data are from Bogorad et al (4).

These "neutral type" results on the effects of electro-polishing on tensile and
ductility properties are in general agreement with the results cited above for
ECM of 4140 steel.

## Fatigue Properties

Certain machining and finishing operations may increase fatigue strengths
in metals in excess of the as-received properties. A comparison, made by Hyler
(5) of the fatigue strength, depth of cold work, and residual surface stress for
various surface-finishing methods is presented in Table III-5. Note the relatively high compressive stresses and depths of cold work for the surface-rolled,
shot-peened, and ground materials, as compared to those of the electro-

**Table III-5. Effects of Various Surface-Finishing Operations
on Fatigue Strength, Depth of Cold Work, and Residual
Stress for Various Steels[a]**

| Surface Finishing Operation | Fatigue Strength, per cent of Mechanically Polished Value | Depth of Cold Work, in. | Surface Compressive Stress, 1000 psi. |
|---|---|---|---|
| Mechanically polished | 100 | <0.002 | 90 |
| Electro-polished | 70-90 | None | None |
| Lathe turned | 65-90 | 0.020 | – |
| Milled | – | 0.007 | – |
| Ground | 80-140 | – | 110 |
| Surface rolled | 115-190 | 0.040 | 130 |
| Shot peened | 85-155 | 0.020 | 150 |

[a] Data are from W. S. Hyler (5).

polished material. Generally, those processes that result in deep work-hardened layers with high residual compressive stresses will show maximum improvement in fatigue strength.

The effect of ECM on the fatigue strength of Type 403 stainless steel was reported by Zimmel (6). S-N curves showing the effects of ECM and subsequent finishing treatments superimposed on the ECM surfaces on fatigue strength of Type 403 stainless steel are presented in Fig. 3-21. The fatigue-strength results

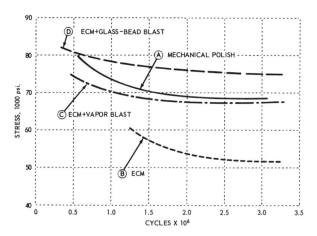

**Fig. 3-21.** Effect of ECM and subsequent surface treatments on fatigue life of Type 403 stainless steel (6).

of treatment $A$ (mechanical polish = 68,000 psi. at $3.1 \times 10^6$ cycles) vs. treatment $B$ (ECM = 51,000 psi. at $3.1 \times 10^6$ cycles) shows the advantage of cold-working the surface. As would be expected, higher fatigue strengths were achieved by mild finishing operations such as vapor blasting (treatment $C$) and bead blast (treatment $D$) after ECM. Even these mild treatments induced compressive stresses in the surface, to the benefit of fatigue strength. Little scatter was noted in the fatigue values of the ECM specimens as opposed to the mechanically processed specimens; this is indicative of the uniform quality of the surfaces that can be produced by the ECMR methods.

The results reported by Zimmel on fatigue studies of ECM specimens fit the general pattern of fatigue results that have been obtained by various workers with electro-polished specimens, indicating that the two processes have a similar effect on the metal surfaces and their fatigue properties (7, 8).

In summary, it should be indicated that in some instances, when the fatigue strength of an ECM or electro-polished metal is compared with that of a mechanically polished or finished metal, the ECM methods will appear to have lowered the fatigue strength or endurance limit by approximately 10 to 25 per cent. The mechanical finishing methods generally impart compressive stresses to the metal surface which raise the fatigue strength. In contrast, ECM and electro-polishing, by removing stressed layers, leave a stress-free surface that allows true fatigue strength to be measured for the metal, *per se*, rather than reflecting that of the metal plus a particular finishing operation.

The conclusion reached is that ECM and electro-polishing are safe methods to use for processing metals. Where fatigue strength is critical, the use of a post-ECM or post-electro-polishing finishing treatment, such as vapor honing or shot-peening is indicated (e.g., see Fig. 3-21, treatments *C* and *D*). These subsequent mechanical treatments can restore or impart compressive stresses to the surface so that the ECM or electro-polished parts, thus treated, will exhibit comparable or better fatigue properties than mechanically finished parts.

### Hydrogen Embrittlement

The question of possible hydrogen pick-up and its effect on ductility and delayed-failure properties arises when dealing with ECM processing of high-strength metals and alloys. Metal removal in ECMR is accomplished by anodic dissolution, so there is no possibility of hydrogen entry or discharge on the workpiece.[1] Hydrogen entry or discharge occurs at the cathode tool surface. If current efficiency at the anode is less than 100 per cent, oxygen or chlorine will be discharged at the workpiece surface.

No instances of hydrogen embrittlement resulting from the ECMR action (anodic dissolution), *per se*, have been reported and none are expected to be reported. Sustained-load and other tests for hydrogen embrittlement after ECMR have all produced negative results. Accordingly, the loss of ductility and the danger of delayed failure due to hydrogen embrittlement are not problems with ECMR-processed parts.

### ECONOMIC CONSIDERATIONS

Accuracy and machining rates provided by ECMR have been discussed as process performance capabilities, yet these are certainly not the only important considerations for general management. Cost should also be considered.

### Operating Costs

ECM machinery is expensive. A complete installation commonly costs from $50,000 to $150,000, depending upon the size and design of the equip-

---

[1]General precautions to observe in rinsing and other handling operations when dealing with hydrogen-sensitive workpieces and acid-type electrolytes are discussed in Reference (1).

ment. Certain special installations cost more and others less. (For instance, if an analysis of all ECMR installations were made at the present time, the median cost would probably be between $12,000 and $15,000.) The figures would be weighted downward heavily by the very large number of electro-chemical grinders in use.

Many of the operating costs of ECM equipment parallel those of more conventional machine tools. Operator cost, shop overhead, and amortization of the capital investment parallel their counterparts on other machines in the shop. However, there are costs which are unique to ECM, specifically, power cost and the cost of the electrolyte. Nevertheless, ECM offers economical operating costs which is certainly one of the primary reasons for installing the machinery.

### Electric Power and Electrolyte

While both ECM and conventional types of equipment require an operator, the ECM machine requires *electric power* and *electrolyte*. It is true that conventional machinery requires coolants, power, etc., but these items are usually familiar in a machine shop. The high currents associated with an ECM machine and the electrolyte required are unfamiliar, and, thus, they require understanding.

First of all, they are not significant cost factors in the use of ECM equipment. Fig. 3-22 is a graph of the power cost/cu in. of material removed vs. the removal

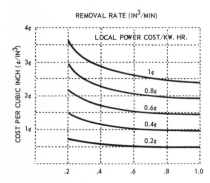

**Fig. 3–22.**   ECM power cost/cu in. material removed vs. removal rate.

rate. Curves are shown for varying local power costs predicated upon the use of a 10,000 amp. installation and a machining voltage of 10 v. The curves are not linear because of the power drawn by the motor on the electrolyte pump which is relatively constant, regardless of the machining rate of the machine tool. The power used in machining, on the other hand, is a linear function of the removal rate. It is the total of these two — pump power and machining power — which forms the total power.

Note that the highest cost of metal removal on the graph is for a low machining rate and a high power cost, 1 cent/kw hr. Even under these adverse circumstances, the power cost is only $3^2/_3$ cents/cu in. of metal removed. This is certainly not a significant cost factor when machining difficult-to-cut alloys or complex three-dimensional forms.

Nor is the electrolyte as costly as one might believe. Most ECM users employ sodium chloride (NaCl) as an electrolyte, and salt is very inexpensive. The price varies somewhat, depending upon the quantity purchased and the locality of the purchaser, but the normal price is about 1 cent/lb.

With proper installation, it is possible to remove 1.0 cu. in. of metal with 5 lbs. of salt, or an electrolyte cost of 5 cents/cu. in. of metal removed. The cost of power and electrolyte are both directly proportional to the metal removed. Power and electrolyte costs for a 10,000 amp. installation, operating at capacity (removing 1.0 cu. in. of metal per min.), are roughly 7 cents/min. When this 10,000 amp. installation is operating at one-half capacity, the costs are roughly $3^{1}/_{2}$ cents/min.; the cost at one-quarter of the system's capacity is about $1^{3}/_{4}$ cents/min.

ECG voltages are generally much lower than ECM voltages, thus the power usage (watts) per cu. in. of metal removed in ECG is much lower than in ECM. ECG is most widely used for grinding tungsten carbide and proprietary electrolytes are used for this work which cost much more than NaCl.

## Tooling

Tooling introduces another element of cost for the prospective ECM user. The tooling is unique because, substantially, it does not wear. The only part of the process which does tend to produce wear is the abrasion of the electrolyte as it passes over the electrode, but this abrasion will not induce measurable wear until many thousands of parts have been produced.

ECM tooling design is a new, rapidly growing science. Unusual materials must be used: brass, copper, stainless steel, and plastics. The beginner will not readily see practical ways for transmitting the high currents required to the electrode and workpiece, or for protecting metal portions of the tooling from unwanted extraneous attack. These problems are not major obstacles to the acceptance of ECM machinery on the shop floor. They do mean, however, that a company contemplating the installation of ECM machinery should employ an engineer who will specialize in the process, who has the capabilities to quickly absorb the necessary new knowledge, and who has the time to adequately supervise the ECM installation(s).

Fundamentally, ECM tooling is not any more complicated than conventional machine tooling. The latter has merely been used longer, is more widely described and discussed in the literature, and is better understood by the average man on the shop floor.

## Economic Advantages

The primary reason that companies in the metalworking fields are installing ECM equipment is that it can generally make a better product for less money. These financial savings are realized because ECM processes, in summary, can offer:

1) High metal-removal rates for the tough or hard alloys.
2) Rapid metal-removal rates when machining complex three-dimensional surfaces.
3) The ability to machine complex three-dimensional surfaces without burrs and without the striation marks left by milling cutters.

4) Freedom from metallurgical damage.
5) Accuracy and economy through the inherent characteristics of the processes.

### REFERENCES

1. J. A. Gurklis, "Metal Removal by Electrochemical Methods and Its Effects on Mechanical Properties of Metals," *DMIC Report 213* (Columbus: Battelle Memorial Institute, January 7, 1965).
2. _____, "Effects of ECMR on Mechanical Properties of Metals," *ASTME Paper EM66–166* (April, 1966).
3. J. Krieg, "Evaluation of the Electrolytic Metal Removal Process for Application on 4140 Alloy Steel (Electroshaping)," *Report 8902,* Contract No. AF 33(657)–7749 and BPSN: 2(8–7381)–73812 (July 10, 1962).
4. L. Ya. Bogorad, S. Ya. Grilikhes, and R. S. Arson, "Electropolishing Steel," as cited by Fedot'ev, N. P., and Grilikhes, S. Ya., "Electropolishing, Anodizing, and Electrolytic Pickling of Metals," Robert Draper Ltd., Teddington, England, 1959, pp. 135–136.
5. W. S. Hyler, "Effect of Cold Work on Fatigue," *SAE Paper,* Iron and Steel Technical Committee's Shotpeening Division Meeting (May 6, 1958).
6. L. J. Zimmel, "An Analysis of Effects of ECM on Fatigue of 403 SS," *Paper,* National Aeronautics and Space Engineering Meeting (October 5–9, 1964).
7. C. L. Faust, "Surface Preparation by Electropolishing," *Journal of the Electrochemical Society, 95* (3) (March, 1949), 62C–72C.
8. A. T. Steer, J. K. Wilson, and O. Wright, "Electropolishing – Its Influence on Fatigue-Endurance Limit of Ferrous and Non-Ferrous Parts,"*Aircraft Production, 15* (July, 1953), 177.

# CHEMICAL MATERIAL
# REMOVAL

The use of chemicals to remove material is an old art. It is known to have been practiced back to the time of the early Egyptians for decorative purposes and, since the 17th century, for decoration and printing applications.

The process remained an art until shortly before World War II when several companies in the United States began to adapt the process to industrial manufacturing. The initial work was primarily directed toward the production of reticles for gun and bomb sights, but rapidly expanded into many other areas. During World War II, North American Aviation, Inc. initiated a program using chemicals to remove unwanted metal from aircraft parts. This particular process, the Chem-Mill Process,[1] constituted the first volume production use of chemical material removal.

Almost simultaneously with the North American Aviation developments, chemicals began to be used to remove unwanted copper from copper-insulator laminates in the then-new field of printed circuits. In the late 1940's and early 1950's, the use of chemicals to completely "chemically blank" functional parts from thin metal sheet was initiated. The technology of this process was rather closely held and did not emerge as a generally available process until the early 1960's.

Chemical engraving, or the use of chemicals to inscribe nomenclature on parts and panels (an obvious extension of the photo-engravers art), did not become commercially significant until the latter part of the 1950's.

The common tie among these 3 chemical material removal processes is the use of acids and alkaline solutions to etch away unwanted material, leaving the final desired pattern or part. Here the similarity ends, and each must be considered as a separate process within the family of chemical material removal processes. Subsequent sections of this chapter cover each in detail, presenting their similarities, differences, techniques, and applications.

## PROCESS PARAMETERS

Since the fundamentals of chemical material removal involve the application of an acid or alkaline resistant material to certain portions of the workpiece, and subsequent application of an etchant removes desired material, the 2 most important factors in the process are the etchant resistant material (known as a maskant or a resist), and the selection of the etchant used to remove the material.

---

[1]The Chem-Mill Process is a patented and licensed process belonging to North American Aviation, Inc., and exclusively licensed to Turco Products, Inc., which, in turn, sub-licenses the process to users.

This section discusses the development of the various maskants and etchants, and gives general selection information as to which type should be used for a particular job.

## Maskants and Resists

The 3 classifications of maskants and resists in general use today are: cut and peel maskants, photographic resists, and screen resists.

**Cut and Peel Maskants.** The cut and peel maskants, which are used almost exclusively for chemical milling of aircraft, missile, and structural parts, are characterized by:

1) The maskant is applied to the entire part to be processed by flow, dip, or spray coating.
2) The materials are relatively thick in nature, being .001 to .005 in. thick in dry film form.
3) The materials are removed from areas to be etched by cutting the maskant with a scribe knife (generally with a template to aid accuracy) and peeling away the unwanted areas.
4) Because of the inherent nature of the maskant and the thickness of the coating, extremely high chemical resistance is achieved, permitting etching depths of .5 in. or more.
5) The materials used for maskants afford flexibility in the processing in that, after a certain area has been etched, additional maskant may be removed so that step etching is possible.

Generally, cut and peel maskants are used where extremely critical dimensional tolerances are not required. Due to the use of templates and scribing, it is very difficult to hold tolerances much tighter than ±.005 in. on the acid resistant image. This does not mean, however, that high accuracies of *etch depth* are not achievable, since they are not dependent upon the image itself.

The maskant type of chemical material removal is generally used for parts which: (1) are extremely large, (2) have many irregularities, (3) require depth of etch in excess of .050 in. from one side, and (4) have multiple level steps in the removal areas.

Such maskants would not be used for: (1) thin materials where the scribing and peeling could distort the material being etched, (2) large numbers of small parts where photographic resists could be utilized at substantial time and cost savings over the hand-scribing techniques, and (3) parts requiring extremely high accuracies, such as motor laminations, television shadow masks, or razor heads.

The types of maskants currently available include vinyl, neoprene, and butyl base materials. Generally the materials are interchangeable. The neoprene and butyl materials, individually or in combination, have slightly greater acid resistance and are generally used to chemically mill titanium and steel alloys. They also can be scribed for multiple-level etching, and then peeled as the individual steps are exposed.

The dry film thicknesses of these materials go up to .008 in. A gallon of these materials will cover 35 to 40 sq. ft. and cost approximately $3.50 to $4.00/gal.

**Photoresists.** The photographic resists are materials which produce etchant resistant images by means of photographic techniques. When exposed through a high-contrast negative, the materials can generally produce either a positive or negative image of the negative itself. Both positive and negative working resists are available, but are used for different purposes.

There is a broad variety of photographic resists, consisting of both naturally-occurring and manufactured resins which, when modified, have photo-sensitive properties, i.e., can be selectively removed by development after exposure to light. Photoresists are generally characterized by:

1) Generation of extremely thin coatings which produce extremely high detail, but lack the chemical resistance necessary for deep etching.

2) Poor bonding of the resist film to the material being etched, unless the material is very carefully cleaned prior to application of the resist.

3) Sensitivity to light and susceptibility to damage by rough handling and exposure to dirt and dust, necessitating careful handling and a clean environment for successful operation.

4) More complicated processing than required by the scribe and peel maskants described above.

Photoresists can be applied by dip, spray, flow, roll coating, and (experimentally) by laminating. Since they are generally applied in liquid form, a drying cycle is required prior to exposure.

All photographic resists currently in use are sensitive to ultraviolet light, but not to normal light found in a manufacturing plant (with the exception of fluorescent lights). Either gold fluorescent or tungsten light of relatively high illumination levels can be used without danger of exposing the resists. Sunlight and standard fluorescent lighting should be avoided. Typical exposure times for photoresists run from 1.0 to 8 minutes, depending upon the type of resist, the thickness of coating, and the etchant used.

Developing, or washing off areas to be etched, is accomplished in developing solutions tailored to fit the particular resist. Following this operation, an additional baking cycle is generally required to increase the chemical resistance of the resist.

Photoresists are generally used for:

1) Thin materials ranging from .00015 to .030 in. thick. The upper limit is generally set by the chemical resistance of the photographic resist.

2) Parts requiring dimensional tolerances of the etchant resistant image tighter than ±.005 in. Image accuracies of ±10 millionths of an inch are achievable with certain resists, and all of the photographic resists can hold tolerances tighter than ± .0005 in.

3) Parts produced in high volume where the chemical resistance of the photographic resists is adequate. Since photographic techniques are adaptable to fully automatic processing, the labor involved in other forms of masking operations can be eliminated and machinery can be designed to produce parts automatically.

Photographic resists are not generally used: (1) for depths in excess of .050 in. thick, (2) on parts larger than 3 ft. by 5 ft., or (3) on materials requiring the use of extremely-active etchants which will degrade or strip the photoresists (e.g., René 41, Inconel X, and Waspalloy).

**Screen Resists.** Screen resists are materials which can be applied to the workpiece through normal silk screening techniques, i.e., the material is applied through a silk or stainless steel mesh which has a stencil placed upon it to prevent deposition of resist in areas that will be subsequently etched. While the stencils are generally made photographically, printing accuracy does not approach that of photographic printing. The image accuracies are, however, better than can generally be achieved by the cutting and peeling of maskants.

Coating thickness deposited by screen printing is intermediate between the photographic resists and the cut and peel maskants. Therefore, the chemical resistance is substantially higher than the photographic resists, but lower than that of the dip or flow coated maskants.

Screen printing has the advantage of being an extremely rapid method of producing a large number of parts to moderate accuracies. The process steps involved include: (1) cleaning the material to remove dirt and oil films, (2) applying the resist by screen printing, (3) drying the image either by air or baking cycle, and (4) etching of part.

Screen printing is generally restricted to: (1) parts no larger than 4 ft. by 4 ft., (2) parts having only flat surfaces or very moderate contours, (3) parts where depth of etch does not exceed .060 in. in depth from one side, and (4) parts which do not require etchant resistant image accuracy higher than ±.004 in.

### Selection of Maskant or Resist

The factors that affect the selection of a resist or maskant for use in chemical material removal are: (1) chemical resistance required, (2) number of parts to be produced, (3) detail or resolution required, (4) size and shape of parts, (5) economics, and (6) ease of removal.

As in most selection processes, choosing a resist or maskant is generally a compromise between the various desirable and undesirable characteristics of the materials involved. The following is a general discussion of these characteristics.

**Chemical Resistance.** The most important characteristic of a maskant or resist is its chemical resistance which varies over a wide range: from the ability to withstand concentrated acids and alkaline solutions for periods of *several hours* for certain of the chemical milling maskants, to *several minutes* usable life in dilute etchants for certain of the modified photo-engraving resists.

A general discussion of the chemical resistance of a resist would be misleading because a number of factors about the situation must be known such as: type of resist, thickness of resist, type of material to which it is applied, surface preparation of the material, etchant used, and operating conditions of the etching solution. Any one of these factors can affect the usable life of a resist or maskant by an order of magnitude or more. Experimental evaluation under actual conditions is the only feasible method of determining the suitability of a particular resist.

Generally speaking, there is a correlation between the thickness of the resist and its chemical resistance, providing that a satisfactory bond can be achieved between the resist and the material being etched. For this reason, relatively thick coatings of chemical milling maskants permit extended exposure to etching. In addition, these materials have very good adhesion to the materials normally used in chemical milling deep-etch work, resulting in minimal attack at the interface between the resist and the metal.

Photoresists, on the other hand, because of their extremely thin film thickness, have substantially lower chemical resistance and are generally not used for etching thicknesses greater than .050 in. in depth. In addition, photoresist materials generally do not have the good adhesion characteristics of the chemical milling maskants and, therefore, the problem of interfacial attack is generally more severe.

Another problem unique to photoresists is resist chipping. Most of the photoresists used today are relatively brittle in nature and, when a part has been etched to a point where the resist over-hangs due to undercutting of the material being etched, the unsupported resist can break off and alter the etching characteristics of that immediate area. This can often result in irregular etching with a resultant loss of part tolerance. Chipping is not generally a problem with the thicker materials used in maskants and screen printed resists, because the resist film is thick enough and resilient enough to be self-supporting.

**Number of Parts.** The number of parts to be produced affects the type of resist or maskant used. If a relatively small number of parts are to be made, the time and cost involved in hand-scribing and peeling of a maskant is not prohibitive. However, if high production quantities are planned, it would be better to employ screen printing applied resists with their resultant substantial labor savings. Where great detail is required for production quantities, photographic resists should be used assuming, of course, that their chemical resistance is sufficient for the job. The photographic and screen printed resists have the advantage that they can be fully automated with a substantial labor savings but, due to their lower chemical resistance, are generally used only for thin materials.

**Detail and Accuracy.** The detail and accuracy required in an etchant resistant pattern also affects resist selection. When using scribe and peel maskants, it is generally recommended that the minimum line width on the etchant resistant pattern be not less than .125 in. and that minimum width of areas to be etched (width of cut) be not less than .060 in. Where any great depth of etch is required, these lines should generally be widened so that the minimum line width is at least twice the depth of cut, and the minimum width of cut is .060 in. plus twice the depth of cut or higher.

When using silk screen deposited resists, which are applicable only to shallow cuts, maskant pattern widths can be as narrow as .010 in. with open areas reduced about the same amount.

Using photoresists, line widths and line spacings can be achieved on the order of .0005 in. or tighter. The accuracy of maskant or resist image is on the order of ±.007 in. for cut and peel maskants, ±.003 in. for screen resist patterns, and ±.001 to .0002 in. for photographic resists.

**Size and Shape of Parts.** Maskants which are coated over the entire part and then scribed and stripped can be used on almost any part size or shape. In this respect, such maskants offer greater versatility than other resist methods. Since they can be flow coated or sprayed, parts of an almost unlimited range in size can be processed by this method. Generally, screen and photographic printing are applied only to flat parts and parts curved in one dimension. Due to limitations on screen frame size, machinery sizes, and film sizes (as in the case of photographic printing), these 2 processes are limited to handling parts measuring less than 4 ft. by 4 ft. There are cases, however, where photographic processing has been used on parts up to 4 ft. by 12 ft. by assembling a series of negatives into the required composite image.

**Processing Difficulties.** The processing of scribe and peel maskants is relatively simple and can be handled under normal plant conditions. With the exception of ventilation to remove solvents released as the maskants dry, no special precautions are required. Surface preparation is also relatively simple, generally requiring only solvent cleaning or light chemical or abrasive cleaning, followed by flow, dip, or spray application of the maskant. The actual scribing is done by standard layout techniques or, when production volume justifies it, through the use of templates.

Screen printing of resists requires much cleaner conditions so that dirt will not clog the screen, but, in other respects, processing requirements are similar to maskant materials.

Photographic resists are, without question, the most difficult to use. Extreme cleanliness must be practiced and surface preparation is quite critical. Any dust or dirt on the surface can cause defects in coating, printing, and developing of the photoresist image and, therefore, near clean-room conditions are required for photoresist processing. The number of operations required is substantially higher and most of the process steps are far more critical than with the other types of maskants. If high detail is the objective, however, these requirements are not economically prohibitive.

**Economics.** The cost of maskants varies widely, even within a basic type of maskant or resist. Photographic resists, for example, range in price from $4/gal. to $27/qt., with each having specific applications. Generally, the lower-cost materials require tighter processing control and are used only on volume production lines where the increased control problems can be offset by economic savings. Certain of the very high-priced photoresists are used, in spite of their high cost, because they provide certain advantages in subsequent processing steps such as greater ease of removal.

**Ease of Removal.** In most applications, the resist or maskant must be removed prior to final use of the part. Some maskants and resists can be dissolved by chemical action while the bond between other resists and the etched material cannot be broken without actually dissolving the resistant image. Generally, mechanical action is required to remove the resists in the latter case. For extremely thin, complicated or delicate parts, a resist that can be removed without mechanical action should be used to avoid damage to the part.

### Etchants and Their Selection

The basic purpose of an etchant is to convert a material, e.g., metal, into a metallic salt which can be dissolved in the etchant and, thus, removed from the work surface. Table IV-1 lists commonly-used etchants, their characteristics, and the materials to which they are applicable.

The selection of an etchant is dependent upon numerous factors, some of which are: (1) material to be etched, (2) type of maskant or resist used, (3) depth of etch, (4) surface finish required, (5) potential damage to or alteration of metallurgical properties of the material, (6) speed of material removal, (7) permissible operating environment, and (8) economics of material removal. All of these factors influence etchant selection for a given metal and a given type of part, and interact with each other so that the selection of an etchant for a specific job can be extremely complex and time-consuming. Fortunately, chemical and equipment suppliers generally make this determination for the user.

The following paragraphs discuss these factors in detail; later sections discuss the interaction between these factors in a few specific cases.

**Material.** The material to be etched influences etchant selection in a number of ways. Foremost, of course, is the fact that the selected etchant must attack the material at an acceptable rate of speed. For any given material, e.g., a metal, there might be 20 or 30 basic chemical combinations which can cause etching (or controlled corrosion); of these, however, only a few will have the specific desirable properties for the particular material.

For a uniform rate of attack, the action of the etchant must be wholly or partially independent of: temperature variations, solution agitation, outside impurities, variations in material hardness and grain structure, and variations in impurities and alloying elements in the material being etched. Needless to say, the ideal etchant would be one whose action did not vary with any of these factors. In practice, however, all etchants are affected to some extent by all of these factors, and generally only one or two of these factors can be minimized in a given etchant.

When the material being etched is not a homogeneous material, as might be the case with alclad, surface-hardened steels, or composites such as glass-base epoxy laminates, the characteristics for 2 or more different materials must be considered when optimizing the choice of an etchant.

**Maskant or Resist.** The effects of the maskant or resist chosen will greatly affect the etchant selection for a given job. The etchant selected must not deteriorate the mask material for the period of time that the part is subjected to it. Certain of the peelable maskants can withstand hours of exposure to hot concentrated caustic solutions, while the same etching solution would strip most of the photoresists used today in a matter of seconds. Thus, such resists could not be used to deep-etch aluminum where caustic baths are commonly utilized.

Another sensitive area is the interface between the maskant and the workpiece. Quite often an etchant will not directly attack the resist or maskant, but will attack the interface between the maskant and the material being etched in such a way that the maskant is lifted but not itself damaged. This damage, of course, can result in a rejected part just as easily as damage to the maskant. Interfacial bond is particularly susceptible to attack by strong chemicals and by additive agents designed to modify other etchant characteristics. A notable example is the addition of a few parts per million of surfactants in undercut-inhibiting-baths used in etching magnesium and zinc. The surfactants can cause complete lifting of photographic resists which would normally be resistant to the nitric acid used as the etchant.

Certain maskants and resists are very temperature-sensitive in that they will act as a proper maskant at one temperature, but fail completely at temperatures 20° to 30°F. higher. Since many etchant baths are exothermic in nature and generate localized hot spots where large areas are being etched, temperature-

## Table IV-1. Etchant Characteristics and General Applications

| Etchant | Concentration | Temperature (°F.) | Etch Rate (in/min) Fresh Solution | Etch Factor | Metals That Etchants Will Attack |
|---|---|---|---|---|---|
| $FeCl_3$<br>$HNO_3$, HCl, $H_2O$ | 42°Bé[1]<br>1:1:2 | 120°<br>100 to 120° | —<br>— | —<br>— | Alfenol |
| $FeCl_3$<br>HCl, $HNO_3$,$H_2O$ | 12 to 18°Bé<br>10:1:9 | 120°<br>120° | .001+<br>.001 to .002 | 1.5:1 to 2.0:1<br>2:1 (variable) | Aluminum alloys |
| $FeCl_3$<br>$HNO_3$ | 42°Bé<br>10 to 15% (vol.) | 120°<br>120° | .001<br>.001 | 2:1<br>1.5 to 2.0:1 | Cold rolled steels |
| $FeCl_3$<br>$(NH_4)_2S_2O_8$<br>Chromic acid<br>$CuCl_2$ | 42°Bé<br>2.2 lbs/gal $H_2O$<br>commercially available<br>35°Bé (regenerated) | 120°<br>start at 90 to 120°<br>120°<br>130° | .002<br>.001<br>.0015<br>.00055 | 2.5 to 3.0:1<br>2 to 3:1<br>2 to 3:1<br>2.5 to 3:1 | Copper and its alloys |
| HF or HF:$HNO_3$ | various | — | — | — | Germanium |
| HF or HF:$HNO_3$ | various | — | — | — | Glass |
| HCl:$HNO_3$ | 3:1 | 90 to 100° | .001 to .002 | — | Gold |
| $HNO_3$ | 10 to 15% | 100 to 120° | .0005 to .001 | 1:1 to 2:1 | Hardened tool steel |
| $FeCl_3$ | 42°Bé | 130° | — | — | Inconel |
| $FeCl_3$ | 42°Bé | 130° | — | — | Inconel X |
| Chromic<br>$FeCl_3$ | commercially available<br>40°Bé | 120°<br>120° | .001<br>.001 | 2 to 2.5:1<br>2:1 | Kovar |
| $FeCl_3$ | 42°Bé | 130° | — | — | Lead |

| Material | Etchant | Concentration | Temperature | Etch rate | Ratio |
|---|---|---|---|---|---|
| Magnesium | $HNO_3$ | 12 to 15% (vol.) | 90 to 120° | .001 to .002 | — |
| Moly permalloy | $FeCl_3$ | 42°Bé | 130° | — | — |
| Moly | $H_2SO_4{:}HNO_3{:}H_2O$<br>$HNO_3{:}HCl{:}H_2O$ | 1:1:1 to 5<br>1:1:1 to 2 | 130°<br>— | .001 at 130°<br>variable with temp.<br>— | —<br> |
| Nickel | $FeCl_3$ | 42°Bé | 120° | .0005 to .001 | 1:1 to 3:1 |
| Nickel-iron alloys | $FeCl_3$ | 42°Bé | 120° | .0005 to .001 | 1:1 to 3:1 |
| Nickel-silver alloys | $FeCl_3$<br>Chromic<br>$(NH_4)_2\ S_2O_8$ | 42°Bé<br>commercially available<br>2.2 lbs/gal $H_2O$ | 130°<br>120°<br>90 to 120° | —<br>—<br>— | —<br>—<br>— |
| Phosphor-bronze | $FeCl_3$<br>Chromic<br>$(NH_4)_2S_2O_8$ | 42°Bé<br>commercially available<br>2.2 lbs/gal $H_2O$ | cold (80°)<br>cold (80°)<br>cold (80°) | .0005<br>.0005<br>.0003 | 2:1<br>2:1<br>2:1 |
| Silicon | $HNO_3{:}HF{:}H_2O$ | various | 100 to 120° | slow | — |
| Silicon steel | $FeCl_3$ | 42°Bé | 130° | .001 | 1.5 to 2:1 |
| Silver | $HNO_3{:}H_2O$<br>$FeNO_3$ | 50 to 90%<br>36°Bé | 100 to 120°<br>120° | .0005 to .001<br>.0008 | —<br>— |
| Stainless steel | $FeCl_3$ | 42°Bé | 130° | .0008 | 1.5 to 2:1 |
| Tin | $FeCl_3$ | 42°Bé | 130° | — | — |
| Titanium | $HF$<br>$HF{:}HNO_3{:}H_2O$<br>$NH_4HF_2{:}HCl{:}H_2O$ | 10 to 50% (vol.)<br>various<br>various | 100 to 120°<br>100 to 120°<br>100 to 120° | | —<br>—<br>— |
| Zinc | $HNO_3$ | 10 to 15% (vol.) | 100 to 120° | .001 | — |

¹Baumé Specific Gravity Scale.

sensitive resists must be avoided or bath temperatures operated low enough so that the localized hot spots do not deteriorate the resist.

**Surface Finish and Etch Depth.** The surface finish required in an etched area has a substantial effect on etchant selection. Certain etchants will attack grain boundaries in a metallic surface and produce uneven etching. Others produce smuts or scum on the surface of the part being etched, which generally cause irregularities in the etching rate over the surface which, in turn, causes surface unevenness. While such etchants are generally considered undesirable, this is not the case when a surface roughness is needed for subsequent adhesion of paint, or filling material, e.g., in chemical engraving.

While other etchants produce a slightly roughened surface compared to the original finish of the part, this roughness is not a function of depth of etch; therefore, it does not affect overall accuracy of the depth of etch even though some deterioration of surface finish results. Some etchants maintain very high surface finish over localized areas but are subject to severe variations in etch rate over extremely small areas, resulting in a pebbled appearance which generally becomes worse as the depth of etch is increased. Etchant selection in this case would depend upon the final application of the part itself.

Since surface finish is generally one of the critical parameters in chemical material removal, substantial effort has been expended to develop modifiers for etching baths that will produce smooth surface finishes. However, some modifiers have undesirable side effects which make the etching bath more sensitive to material variations and process variations as described earlier.

**Damage to Material.** A notable characteristic of chemical material removal is that it does not generally damage the material while removing a portion of that material. However, there are possible combinations of materials and etchants that result in hydrogen embrittlement and/or enhancement of stress corrosion cracking which reduce fatigue strength of the part. In addition, incomplete removal of an etchant from a work surface can cause any number of problems in the end operation of the part. Certain etchants tend to be more active if they are not completely removed, while others are more easily neutralized and removed to prevent subsequent part deterioration. This problem has not been of particular concern to the metalworking industry; however, it is a definite factor in selecting etchants for metal removal in electronic circuits, and in the etching of non-metallics used in electrical circuits.

**Material Removal Rate.** In selecting an etchant, material removal rate is always a major factor. If all other factors are equal, the faster a part is etched the more economically it can be produced. However, theory and practice are far apart in this instance because faster etchants generally tend to have many severe side effects, including: (1) reduction in surface finish, (2) increased undercutting, (3) higher heating, (4) a greater change of etch rate with temperature, (5) reduced capacity for holding metal salts in solution, and (6) attack on the bond between maskants and the workpiece.

With a few exceptions, the etch rate is generally limited to .001 to .002 in/ min if acceptable parts are to be produced. There are certain cases, wherein accuracy and surface finish have not been critical, where production etch rates of .005 to .007 in/min have been achieved. Although these penetration rates are relatively low, very large areas can be worked and, therefore, overall metal removal rates can be quite high. An existing installation in the aircraft industry is currently removing in excess of 517 cu. in/hr of aluminum in a chemical machining line.

**Operational Environment.** The operational environment prevailing in a chemical material removal facility also affects etchant selection. Certain materials, such as hydrofluoric acid, nitric hydrofluoric acid mixtures, and mixtures of other very active acids, quite often can be utilized as etchants from a theoretical standpoint, but are not feasible because of inherent toxological problems. Other limiting factors, such as the evolution of poisonous or explosive gases, the generation of large quantities of heat which cannot be extracted from etching baths, and the disposal of waste etchants, can sometimes preclude the use of an etchant that is otherwise chemically and metallurgically acceptable.

**Economics.** When several etchants exist which can perform an adequate technical job, cost factors sometimes dictate the one selected. Where high-detail chemical engraving is required and the total amount of material being removed is minor, a very high-cost etchant can be used. However, where a bulk of material is to be removed, etchant cost can be a deciding factor in the selection of the process.

A number of factors must be considered in the economic evaluation of etchants, including: (1) initial cost of chemicals, (2) cost of maintaining chemicals during their usable life, (3) control equipment necessary to maintain etching solutions, (4) cost of etchant disposal when it is depleted, and (5) the value of any by-products produced.

Etching costs can range from very expensive (in the case of costly chemicals which can remove very little metal per unit/volume and are expensive to dispose of) down to a negative cost factor where the by-products produced in etching are worth more than the initial chemicals used in the process. An example of a very expensive etchant is nitric-hydrofluoric-sulfuric acid materials used to etch epoxy glass laminates; an example of a negligible cost etchant is ferric nitrate used to etch silver where recovery of the silver more than pays for the chemicals. Another similar example is cupric chloride used to etch copper where the resulting recovery of copper materials more than offsets the cost of the chemicals used.

## Applications

It is impossible to generalize as to which chemical material removal process should be used to produce parts unless a detailed description of the part, the quantity required, and the tolerance factors involved are known. To illustrate the problem, 4 different aluminum parts of varying sizes, shapes, and required quantities are discussed below. In each case, actual production of the parts has shown that they can be produced more economically by chemical machining than by conventional metalworking techniques. In addition, they demonstrate the range of processing technology available within the chemical material removal art, each part having been produced in a manner which would not be acceptable for any of the other parts.

**Aircraft Wing Skin.** The aircraft part shown in Fig. 4-1 is an aluminum wing skin, 8 ft. by 16 ft., with numerous surface areas etched to remove metal unnecessary for structural purposes. Tolerances on the location of the pockets

**Fig. 4–1.** Aluminum aircraft wing skin with numerous surface areas etched to remove unnecessary metal for better strength-to-weight ratio. *(Courtesy, Chemcut Corporation)*

was fractional in nature, but the depth of etch, and therefore the amount of material removed, was critical to within a few thousandths of an inch. Production requirements were 50 to 100 parts.

The selection of a maskant for this part was based primarily upon the depth of etch and dimensional tolerances required. The maskant used was a standard elastomeric material which was flow coated and then scribed with the required pattern. Since step etching was required, it was essential that the material used be capable of being re-cut and additional areas exposed to etching in subsequent processing steps. Because of the size of the part and the depth of etch, neither photographic nor screen resists could be used; in this case, a clear-cut decision between maskants and resists could be made.

Selecting an etchant was, again, quite simple because the part was too large to be placed in any available spray system and, therefore, deep tank etching was required. Due to the depth of etch tolerances required, a standard proprietary alkaline etchant was used. These solutions give a uniform rate of attack on large parts in still or air-agitated tank etching. The etchants were specifically designed for this type of operation and do not work effectively in spray or splash etching systems.

**Helicopter Vent Screen.** The aluminum vent screen (see Fig. 4-2) used in helicopter manufacturing (in a relatively low volume of 15 to 30 parts) was made to tolerances on the order of ±.010 in. from different types of aluminum. The material was .062 in. thick and could be etched from both sides.

The selection of an acid resist for the screen was based primarily upon the relatively high detail and complexity and permissible tolerances involved in the part. In this case, a standard lacquer-base screening material was applied to the part through a silk screen on a semi-automatic printing machine. Both sides of the part were printed with acid resist so that etching was accomplished from both sides. It would have been possible to use photographic resists in this case, but the tolerances did not require the high detail provided by the photographic resist and, therefore, the relatively high costs of this method were not justified.

A conveyorized spray etching machine was used with hydrochloric acid as the etchant. The rate of attack was very high, on the order of .005 in/min, and the previously mentioned 517 cu. in. of metal removal per hour was achieved. The selection of hydrochloric acid as the etchant was based upon economic factors. The slightly roughened and uneven etch that results when HCl is used to etch at these rates did not affect overall part performance, and the increase in speed and decrease in cost of production were more than justified.

**Instrument Panel.** A front panel of an oscilloscope (see Fig. 4-3), which required high detail engraving, was chemically engraved in quantities of 500 to

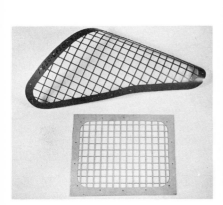

**Fig. 4-2.** Aluminum helicopter vent screens. *(Courtesy, Chemcut Corporation)*

**Fig. 4-3.** High detail engraving on front panel of oscilloscope. *(Courtesy, Chemcut Corporation)*

1000 parts. Relatively high detail—lines on the order of .005 to .007 in. wide—had to be held in the production process.

The high-detail nomenclature was etched on the front of a previously blanked aluminum sheet. Because of the detail necessary, the resist printing process required the maximum available resolution, and, therefore, a photographic resist was used.

The etching requirements were also tight because it was desirable that there be a minimum amount of undercut so that detail was not lost and, secondly, that there be a slightly roughened surface in the bottom of the etched nomenclature so that filling inks would adhere to the surface and provide a durable panel. In this case, either modified ferric chloride baths or proprietary etchants could be used. The latter was chosen and, although the cost of these etchants was extremely high relative to HCl, the volume of material being removed was quite low; therefore, an acceptable cost per part was achieved as well as the high detail required. Because etching depth was only .003 to .005 in., a low-cost photoresist could be used since the time of exposure to the etchant was short.

**Reactor Sample Holder.** The nuclear reactor sample holder shown in Fig. 4-4 was etched in soft aluminum .032 in. thick. It had to be burr-free and was required in very small volume. Because of the low volume, photographic processing techniques were used. A photoresist with substantially higher chemical resistance than that used on the instrument panel was needed because of the thickness of the part. Although parts tolerances were not high, it was essential that the photographic image be as accurate as possible because process uncertainties in etching this thickness of material would take up most of the tolerance available. The resist used was a polymeric material specifically designed for deep etching of metals. The etchant used was a modified ferric chloride bath with inhibitors designed to slow down the etching rate in the bath to approximately .0015 in/min, thus producing a more uniform etch.

**Fig. 4–4.** Nuclear reactor sample holder etched in soft aluminum. *(Courtesy, Chemcut Corporation)*

As these examples show, chemical material removal can accomplish a wide variety of processing. The actual selection of the process is dependent upon a large number of factors and each job requires specific consideration before the best and most economical process can be determined.

## CHEMICAL MILLING

The 3 chemical material removal processes to be described in the following sections are: chemical milling, chemical blanking, and chemical engraving. The art of chemical milling (CHM), while it draws on the photo-engravers' experience, is a unique invention of the aircraft industry as discussed in the introduction to this chapter. CHM is the process used to shape metals to an exacting tolerance by the chemical removal of metal, or deep etching of parts, rather than by conventional mechanical milling or machining operations. The amount of metal removed, or depth of etch, is controlled by the amount of immersion time in the etching solution. The location of the unetched or unmilled areas on a part is controlled by masking or protecting these areas from the action of the etchant solution.

The CHM process consists of 5 main steps: cleaning, masking, scribing, etching, and demasking.

### Cleaning

Thorough cleaning is necessary to insure uniform adhesion of the maskant and uniform chemical dissolution of the metals. When cleaning a refractory such as tungsten, the cleaning procedure may vary from solvent wipe only, to flash etching, depending on the soil present and the porosity of the metal. The more porous the material, the more difficult it is to clean because of the entrapment of the cleaning solutions. Therefore, solvent wiping or vapor degreasing is generally preferred. In general, when cleaning aluminum, magnesium, steel, or titanium alloys, the major aircraft companies follow standard cleaning procedure, i.e., vapor degreasing, alkaline cleaning and deoxidizing, whereas many of the chemical milling suppliers who serve the aircraft industry simply solvent-wipe prior to chemical milling. Descaling parts is seldom necessary but is sometimes required because the maskant sticks much too tightly to a corroded or scaled surface to be conveniently removed in the scribing operation. After cleaning, the parts are allowed to stand until dry.

### Masking

The mask is applied by either dip, flowcoat, or airless spray techniques, depending on part size and configuration. Two or more coats are applied to aluminum and magnesium parts, while 4 or more are applied to steel, titanium, tungsten, and other refractories in order to obtain sufficient protection from the etchant.

After the last coat is tack-free, aluminum and magnesium parts are air-cured for from 3 to 24 hrs., depending on individual plant schedules and storage space. In general, it is best to let the part air-cure overnight when possible. Steel, titanium, and the refractory alloys may be oven-baked for $1/2$ hr. at 225°F. to increase the etchant resistance of the mask and decrease the flow time.

### Scribing

Patterns are placed on the masked and cured part by using a template as a guide and scribing the mask with a fine knife. The chemical milling template (CMT) as shown in Fig. 4-5, can be made of epoxy-impregnated fiberglass, or

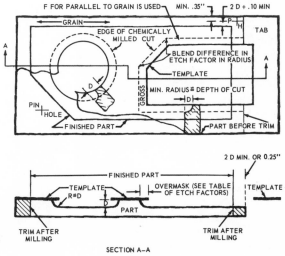

**Fig. 4-5.** Typical chemical milling template (CMT).

aluminum or steel template stock. Fiberglass templates are the most common since they work best on curved surfaces. Fig. 4-6 shows an 8-step template and the part it was used to make. Each cut-out or separate cut is color coded so that the scriber knows which cut is to be made first. In many cases, all cuts can be made at one time, thus reducing handling time considerably by eliminating the racking and unracking and handling to and from the scribing area of these rather large parts.

**Fig. 4-6.** Eight-step template and the part it produced.

The fiberglass template can be made by simply laying it up on a formed and scribed blank part, or laying it up in a plaster splash pattern. The blank part is scribed with the desired pattern as determined by the inspection template. When the template is removed from the part, it will have picked up the lines which are then used as a guide in making the proper cut-outs. Metal templates are made in the usual manner.

Since the template is used as a guide for the scribing operation, it must be made with great care and precision in order to insure close land width tolerances. Many small tools are used in the process. A fine knife is used to cut the mask except when the scribe line is in an inaccessible area, such as the leading edge of a wing. A hot knife is used in such cases which is very similar to a soldering iron except that it has a sharp tip. The tip, when hot, simply melts the mask. However, the line definition is not as good with the hot knife as with the fine knife. Other

**Fig. 4-7.** Hand stripping mask from scribed part.

**Fig. 4-8.** Parts racked in baskets ready for immersion in etching solution.

small tools used include: tape for patching the mask, tape rollers, rubber stoppers for plugging tool holes, and cliquot pliers and pins.

After the part is scribed, the mask is hand stripped from the part, leaving the areas to be milled exposed to the etching solution as shown in Fig. 4-7. The parts are carefully measured with a micrometer or other device to determine the initial thickness. The initial thickness minus the final thickness gives the depth of cut. The exact immersion time in the etchant can then be determined by multiplying the depth of cut in mils by the etch rate in mils/min.

### Etching

The prepared parts are racked in baskets (see Fig. 4-8) and milled by immersion in a suitable etchant solution until the proper depth of cut has been obtained. The parts are rotated during the etching cycle to insure uniform etching and fillet radii. Figs. 4-9 and 4-10 show a new type basket which reduces racking time and part damage. The parts are placed in the basket like eggs in a carton.

**Fig. 4-9.** Racking basket designed to reduce racking time and part damage.

**Fig. 4-10.** In this racking basket, parts can be inserted like eggs in a carton to prevent damage and ensure etching of each part.

Special etchants have been prepared for the exotic and refractory alloys. For the most part these etchants are combinations of raw acids that are very corrosive, not only to the alloy being etched, but also to the surrounding structure. It is desirable, therefore, to have the etch tanks outside or at least in a separate building.

Rinsing (and de-smutting in the case of aluminum) completes the cycle.

### Demasking

Mask removal is accomplished by hand stripping or by immersing the masked part in a suitable demasking solution. After the parts are demasked, cleaned, and inspected, they are sent to the routing area where they are trimmed to final dimension (see Fig. 4-11). The routing tool template may be similar to a chemical milling template or be of heavy duty steel construction.

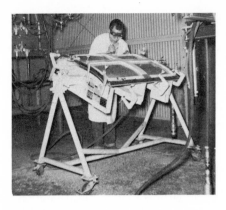

**Fig. 4-11.**    Routing and/or trimming operation.

## Process Parameters

The following discussions apply to normal production parts. If tolerances or dimensions are desired which are not discussed, prototype parts should first be made in order to establish methods and costs.

**Depth of Cut.** Although cuts up to 2 in. have been made in plate stock by CHM, the following maximum depths obtainable can be used as a guide:

Sheet and plate      .500 in. maximum depth/surface
Extrusions           .150 in. maximum depth/surface
Forgings             .250 in. maximum depth/surface

**Depth of Cut Tolerance.** Since the etchant solutions used in CHM reproduce the thickness variations of the original raw stock, the tolerances obtainable are difficult to predict. Table IV-2 can be used as a guide to the removal rates

**Table IV-2. Removal Rates and Tolerances for Chemical Milling**

| Material | Depth of Etch per min. (in.) | Total Depth of Cut (in.) | Milling Tolerance (in.) |
|---|---|---|---|
| Aluminum | .001 | up to .020 | ±.001 |
| | | .021 to .060 | ±.002 |
| Magnesium | .0013 | up to .020 | ±.001 |
| | | .021 to .060 | ±.002 |
| | | greater than .060 | ±.003 |
| Stainless steel and heat-resistant alloys | .005 | up to .020 | ±.001 |
| | | .021 to .060 | ±.002 |
| | | greater than .060 | ±.003 |
| Titanium alloys | .005 | up to .020 | ±.002 |
| | | .021 to .060 | ±.0035 |
| | | greater than .060 | ±.005 |

and tolerances that can be expected when chemical milling various materials. When forging or machining operations precede CHM, the final tolerances must either be enlarged to allow for the thickness variations introduced by these operations, or these variations must be removed.

CHM tolerances can be improved by using premium or close tolerance stock, by pre-grinding stock to a close tolerance, by segregating incoming stock according to actual thickness, by individual handling during the etching cycle, or, where possible, by using the narrower widths of standard sheet stock which are controlled to a closer tolerance by the producing mill (see Fig. 4-12). A

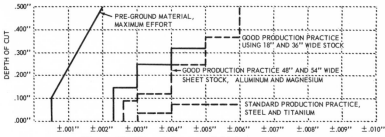

**Fig. 4–12.** Remaining metal thickness tolerance.

reasonable production tolerance for CHM is ±.002 in. plus the actual raw stock tolerance prior to CHM. With these considerations in mind the following tolerances are attainable in production chemical milling:

If the depth of cut is .250 in., the tolerance will be ±.030 in. for both $A$ and $B$ in Fig. 4-13 for normal production. A tolerance of ±.017 to ±.020 in. can be obtained on a .250 in. cut if greater care is used.

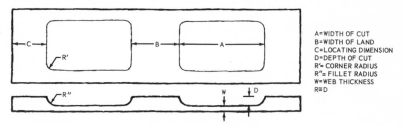

**Fig. 4–13.** Lateral tolerances.

**Minimum Land Width.** The minimum land width should be twice the depth of cut, but not less than .125 in. It need not be greater than 1.0 in. Narrower lands are possible, but more expensive to achieve. Very narrow lands may be made by using the silk screen process (for shallow cuts only), or by using photosensitive masks (see Figs. 4-14 and 4-15).

**Minimum Width of Cut.** The minimum width of cut should be twice the depth of cut plus .060 in. for cuts up to .125 in. deep, and twice the depth of cut plus .125 in. for cuts greater than .125 in. deep (see Fig. 4-15).

**Tapering Parts.** Continuous or true tapers are made by controlling the rate at which parts are lowered into, or withdrawn from, the etchant solution. This type of taper, as shown in Fig. 4-16, should not exceed .010 in. per lineal foot for steel, and .100 in. per lineal foot for aluminum.

Step tapers or step cuts (see Fig. 4-17) are approximations of true tapers achieved by a series of immersions in the etchant solution, with the mask being

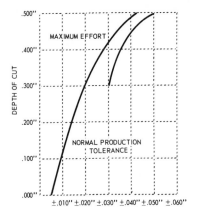

Fig. 4-14. Width of cut and width of land tolerances.

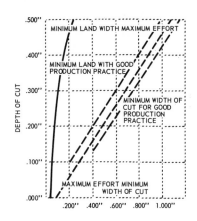

Fig. 4-15. Minimum land width and minimum width of cut.

Fig. 4-16.

Fig. 4-17.

progressively stripped between immersions. This type of taper is often less expensive than the equivalent continuous taper when a part is very complex and has several different tapers. The continuous taper, however, gives a lighter part.

**Grain Direction.** Grain direction should be noted on the blueprint for aluminum parts and, wherever possible, it should be noted in such a way that the longest cut is made parallel to the grain. Fig. 4-18 shows the proper orientation of grain direction with cut. Grid patterns should be laid out at 45 deg. to the grain direction.

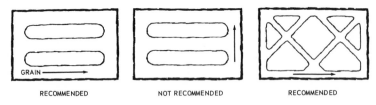

Fig. 4-18.

**Surface Finish.** The surface finish of CHM parts is determined by the initial surface finish, the alloy, the heat-treat condition, and the depth of cut. In general, good quality stock, free from scratches, pits and other damage, should be specified. The following surface finishes can be expected on the metals named:

*Aluminum.* The surface smoothness varies from 70 to 160 rms. depending on alloy and depth of cut. An rms. of 70 to 125 may be expected for cuts up to .250 in., with an average of 90 rms., and an rms. of 80 to 165 may be expected for cuts greater than .250 in., with an average of 115 rms. (Note: surface imperfections are reproduced but not enlarged.)

*Magnesium.* A smooth satin or smooth shiny surface of 30 to 70 rms., with an average of 50 rms., may be expected. Surface imperfections tend to "wash out" or disappear.

*Steel.* Either a smooth shiny or smooth satin surface finish of 30 to 250 rms. can be obtained, depending on alloy, heat-treat, and depth of cut.

*Titanium.* A smooth shiny surface of 15 to 50 rms. can be obtained. The average is 25 rms.

**Stepped Sections.** Stepped sections may be made by progressively unmasking a part. The part may be etched on one side only, or on both sides at one time.

**Trim Area.** Whenever possible, CHM parts should be designed with trim area, which is the excess material surrounding the actual part that is trimmed off after chemical milling. (When no trim area is provided, much time and money is spent in protecting the edge of the part.)

**Chemical Milling After Forming.** Forming material that is uniform in cross-section reduces the possibility of cracking, buckling, or "oil canning." By chemically milling *after* forming, the cost of check and straightening fixtures is greatly reduced. It is extremely difficult, and in many cases impossible, to conventionally machine subsequent to forming.

**Tubing.** The wall thickness of tubing can be reduced or tapered. Hose clamps on thin-wall tubing require additional thickness of material in order to reinforce the compression area. By using heavier wall tubing (which is also easier to bend) for strength at attach points, and reducing the outside diameter to drawing requirements, a stronger lighter part can be made.

### Material Specifications

**Raw Stock.** Stocks should be of the same heat-treat and, where possible, of the same mill run or from the same manufacturer for each group of parts run in order to insure uniformity of physical and chemical structure, and close tolerance control.

**Heat-Treating.** CHM parts should be heat-treated, when necessary, prior to chemical milling.

**Bare Material.** When designing parts that are to be chemically milled from aluminum, bare material should be specified whenever possible because it gives line definition and better fillet radii (see Fig. 4-19).

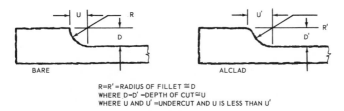

R=R' =RADIUS OF FILLET ≅ D
WHERE D=D' =DEPTH OF CUT≅U
WHERE U AND U' =UNDERCUT AND U IS LESS THAN U'

**Fig. 4-19.**

## Mechanical Properties of Chemically-Milled Materials

When any new process is developed for the manufacture of structural components, or changes are made in existing processes, the major concern of designers is the effect which the process innovation or revision has on the mechanical properties of the material processed. The development of CHM has been accompanied by an increasing number of inquiries regarding the compression, tension, shear, and fatigue properties of chemically milled materials. Although information on all metals and alloys is incomplete at this time, tests on certain alloys in each class of materials discussed below are indicative of the low order of change, in both static and fatigue characteristics, from the parent material.

**Aluminum.** Standard mechanical property tests indicate that CHM has no appreciable effect on the compression, tension, or shear properties of aluminum alloys.

Extensive fatigue data have been submitted on sheet alloys of 2024-T3, T4; 2014; 6061-T6; 7075-T6; and 7178-T6. Tests on 2024-T3 demonstrated that CHM does not reduce the fatigue life of either notched or unnotched specimens. Fatigue tests on 7075-T6, performed at high stress levels, show more favorable results for chemically-milled material than for machine-milled material. Tests on 6061-T6 and 7178 show that CHM does not significantly affect the fatigue life of these alloys. Attach holes produce a greater effect on fatigue life than CHM; parts containing holes need not, therefore, be considered fatigue critical. In addition, chemically-milled materials show greater uniformity of spread or range on the standard S-N fatigue curve than machine-milled materials.

Accelerated corrosion tests have shown that chemically-milled materials are neither more, nor less, susceptible to corrosive attack than machine milled alloys.

**Magnesium.** A Krouse Plate Bending Fatigue Test report has been prepared on AZ-31A, B extruded, and ZK-60A plate material. The stress range tested was 14 to 16 ksi. It was concluded that no appreciable reduction in fatigue life was noted when compared to machined specimens.

**Iron and Nickel Alloys.** Tests on 4340 steel showed that CHM does not affect its tensile properties. Compression and shear properties data for 17-7 PH steel in the THD 1075 condition indicate that the CHM process has no significant effect on these properties. Fatigue tests indicate that there was no difference in the chemically-milled and machine-milled materials. No evidence of intergranular attack or hydrogen embrittlement was found within the specified control limits.

The tensile properties of PH 15-7 Mo Cres steel are not significantly lowered when CHM is performed after the refrigeration treatment, −100°F. for 8 hrs. Nor are the tensile properties of this steel adversely affected by CHM in either the "as received" or the PH 950 condition.

CHM will cause a lowering of the per cent elongation and ultimate tensile strength when AM 350 Cres steel parts are chemically-milled in the "as welded" and " as welded and heat-treated" condition.

Some hydrogen pick-up has been traced in the steel alloys, Vascojet 1000 and Thermold J.

**Titanium.** Mechanical property tests on conventionally milled, and chemically-milled 6Al-4V titanium alloy sheet show that chemical milling has no significant effect on these properties.

Reverse cantilever bending fatigue tests on A-110AT titanium alloy sheet concluded that CHM increased the hydrogen content of this alloy and decreased its fatigue life. Vacuum annealing reduced the hydrogen content.

It has been reported that hydrogen embrittlement is not a serious problem when chemically milling the 8 Mn titanium alloy as long as the initial hydrogen content is kept below 80 ppm. and the part is chemically-milled from one side only to a depth not to exceed $1/2$ of the original stock thickness. None of the other titanium alloys pick up enough hydrogen as a result of CHM to be a problem, except the all-beta alloy, 13V-11Cr-3Al.

### Applications

In general, CHM is used to:
(1) Remove metal from a portion or the entire surface of formed or irregularly-shaped parts such as forgings, castings, extrusions, or formed wrought stock.
(2) Reduce web thicknesses below practical machining, forging, casting, or forming limits.
(3) Taper sheets and pre-formed shapes.
(4) Produce stepped webs, resulting in consolidation of several details into one integral piece.

### Advantages

Machine practicality or conventional machining methods need not limit the designer or manufacturer of chemically-milled parts. For example, a part may be chemically milled on both sides simultaneously and, in so doing, be processed twice as fast while warpage, which might result from the release of "locked in" stresses is minimized.

Many parts can be chemically milled at one time either by processing a large piece before cutting out the parts, or by milling many separate pieces in the tank at one time.

Machined or extruded parts may be reduced overall by machining or extruding a uniform amount oversize prior to CHM. The part shown in Fig. 4-20 was first machined oversize to provide vertical webs, and then reduced all over by CHM to provide web sections that are thinner than can be machined by conventional methods.

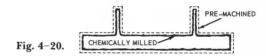

Fig. 4-20.

Extrusions, forgings, castings, formed sections, and deep drawn parts can be lightened considerably by CHM. Raw stock, such as sheet or bar, which would normally be heavier because of the limitations of standard sizes and/or minimum thickness restrictions required for forming, forging, or casting, can also be lightened considerably. Parts may be produced with very thin web sections without fear of excessive warpage or distortion by observing the proper relationship between pocket size and web thickness, and close tolerances can be held. In addition, the tapering of sheets or formed sections can be readily accomplished by CHM and various tapers may be made on one or both sides of a part.

While the heavier ends *A* and *B* of the forging shown in Fig. 4-21 can be formed to the desired thickness, the thin central portion cannot. However, the central portion may be reduced by CHM. The least expensive method of reducing the center is to open up the forging dies at the heavy ends by the amount

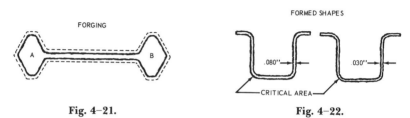

Fig. 4-21.                    Fig. 4-22.

that the thin section is oversize. It is then possible to reduce the entire forging without expensive masking and scribing operations by simply immersing the entire part in the etchant solution.

In order to properly form the hat section shown in Fig. 4-22, .080 in. of stock is required. However, strength requirements can be satisfied with only .030 in. of stock. Therefore, the part is first formed using the heavier stock and then chemically milled to reduce it to the minimum thickness allowed.

Using CHM, a casting can now be designed uniformly oversized, heat-treated with little or no warpage, and then chemically milled to achieve the desired final dimensions. The resultant surface finish can often be reduced from greater than 200 rms. to 40 to 60 rms. Parts manufactured by CHM normally do not require subsequent sanding or polishing of the milled surface.

CHM permits the design of lighter weight, integrally-stiffened parts. The manufacture of such parts is simplified by eliminating riveting, welding (seam, spot, or fusion), metal bonding, or additional stiffeners and doublers normally required for structural stability. CHM designs will allow for the proportional transfer of stresses. In addition, CHM improves the design of sandwich construction parts by leaving heavy bands or stiffeners (integral with one or both skins) at attach points.

Parts may be formed and heat treated prior to the CHM operation. And, since forming is easier prior to the machining operation, less expensive forming dies are required and costly "check and straighten" work is largely eliminated. Warpage resulting from heat-treating is also minimized.

### Limitations

Fillet radii produced by CHM are determined by depth of cut, alloy, etchant, maskant, etc., and are approximately equal to the depth of cut. Inside corners take a spherical shape while outside corners remain sharp.

Aluminum castings are normally difficult to chemically mill, due to the porosity and heterogeneity of the cast material. (Aluminum castings may be chemically milled when neither a smooth surface nor a high strength is required.)

Welded parts must be considered individually because CHM over a welded area often results in pits and uneven etching. Many welded materials can be satisfactorily chemically milled; however, individual tests should be performed to determine the advisability of chemically milling a particular part.

Surface irregularities such as dents and scratches are reproduced in the chemically milled surface of aluminum alloys. Surface waviness and thickness variations are reproduced but not enlarged. On the other hand, surface dents or scratches in magnesium alloys tend to wash out or disappear as a result of chemical milling.

Generally, holes, deep and narrow cuts, narrow lands, and sharp, steep tapers should not be attempted with CHM. Normally, cuts in excess of .500 in. are not recommended.

### Future Potential

The future for CHM is bright. As new products and techniques are developed, the cost per part decreases and the ease of operation increases. If this improvement continues, it will be possible to automate the process, thus making it competitive with other processes for commercial work. Meanwhile, CHM is an invaluable tool in the aerospace industry where weight is important.

## CHEMICAL ENGRAVING

Chemical engraving is the use of the chemical material removal process to produce parts such as name plates, front panels, and other parts which would be conventionally produced on pantograph engraving machines or by die stamping. Two basic methods of chemical engraving are available: those with recessed lettering, and those with raised lettering. Filling may or may not be desired, but is normally used to highlight the image.

Fig. 4-23 shows the sequence steps in a chemical engraving. First, the image

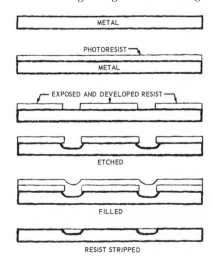

**Fig. 4–23.** Steps in chemical engraving exaggerated to show relative changes.

is placed upon the metal using an acid resistant material which can either be screen printed or photographically printed. The part is then etched to the desired depth, rinsed, and dried. A layer of filling material is then applied over the top of the resist, either by roller coating, spraying, dipping, or flow coating. After the filling enamel has dried, the entire plate is immersed in a stripping solution which removes the resist but does not attack the filling material. The swelling of the resist causes the filling material to be removed from all areas except the recessed areas, leaving a filled image with bare metal showing where the resist has been removed. Subsequent steps may involve applying a protective coating of anodic film, plating, or organic material over the exposed material if such protection is needed.

Another variant of the same process uses anodized aluminum as a substrate rather than bare metal and, thus, produces a chemically engraved image which has anodizing protection on the surface when the resist is removed. This process may also be varied to permit re-anodizing, rather than filling, with enamels to give a totallly anodized aluminum name plate of one or more colors (see Fig. 4-24).

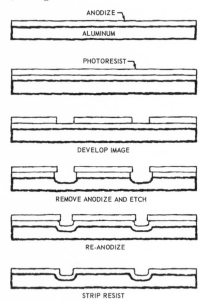

Fig. 4-24. Fully anodized chemically engraved name plate exaggerated to show detail.

## Tooling

The tooling required for chemical engraving is either a photographic positive of the image desired or a silk screen with the inverse image of the desired pattern. Photographic resists require the use of the positive and are generally used on high-detail work or on short-run parts. Silk screening is generally used in longer production runs where the lower tolerances achieved can be permitted. The silk screen method results in a substantial reduction in processing costs due to less costly chemicals and fewer processing steps. The artwork should be generated with undercut compensation included in the original drawings. The undercut, of course, will depend upon the type of metal to be etched and the etchant used.

Tooling costs for a typical front panel, including photographic work and screen manufacturing, would run approximately $10 to $20, depending upon complexity.

## Tolerances

Mechanical tolerances on front panels and name plates generally are not particularly tight—rarely less than ±.005 in. except on letter size and depth of etch. These dimensions are relatively easy to control by initial artwork design and etching time.

## Surface Finish

After the acid resistant image has been applied to the panel, either by photographic techniques or by screen printing, the panel is etched. The chemical etching process produces an ideal shape for subsequent filling with paints because the undercut produces a near-vertical side wall at the surface of the character with a tapered bottom shape in the groove as shown in Fig. 4-25. Ideally, the etchants selected should produce a slightly roughened surface in the areas etched so that the filling paint will adhere well. An ideal surface finish is on the order of 20 to 50 microinches. A mirror finish surface is not particularly desirable from the standpoint of paint adhesion.

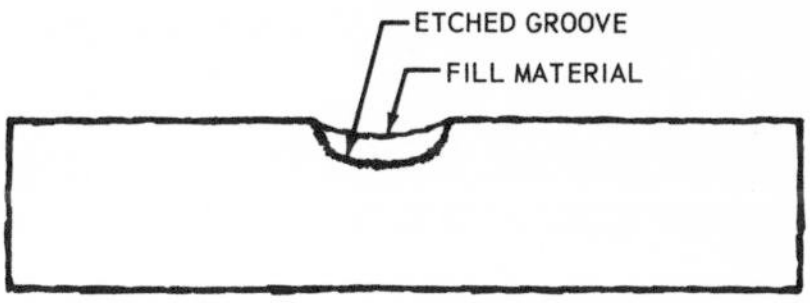

**Fig. 4–25.** Cross-section of chemically engraved part.

## Materials

In general, higher temperatures and lower specific gravities will produce this surface roughness on materials such as aluminum and stainless steel. Materials such as brass and copper are relatively difficult to matte finish in this manner and thus pose some problem in filling.

## Applications

Chemical engraving is generally used when a highly durable product is required and where screen printing or normal labels would not suffice, either for durability or appearance reasons. Nearly all metals can be chemically engraved, with the common metals being aluminum, brass, copper, and stainless steel. The process is particularly advantageous when a large amount of nomenclature is to be inscribed onto one part, such as instrument front panels and motor name plates. Fig. 4–26 shows typical applications of chemical engraving.

In addition to this application, chemical engraving should be used when extremely fine detail is required, or where a hard-to-work metal (such as stainless steel) is needed for endurance purposes. With few exceptions, it is less expensive to chemically engrave than use conventional engraving on flat work. However,

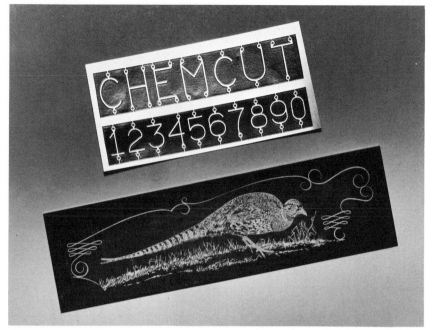

**Fig. 4–26.** Typical chemical engraving applications. *(Courtesy, Chemcut Corporation)*

for non-metallics, curved work, or one-of-a-kind items, conventional engraving is preferred.

## CHEMICAL BLANKING

Chemical blanking is the process of producing metallic and non-metallic parts by chemical action. Basically, the process consists of placing a chemical resistant image of the part on a sheet of metal and exposing the sheet to chemical action which dissolves all of the metal except the desired part. Fig. 4-27 shows a variety of parts produced by chemical blanking.

### Photochemical Blanking

The photographic resist process of chemical blanking is by far the most common one in use today. Fig. 4-28 shows the process steps involved. The metal can be chemically cleaned in numerous ways, including degreasing, pumice scrubbing, electro-cleaning, or chemical cleaning.

The cleaned metal is coated with photographic material which, when exposed to light of the proper wave length, will polymerize and remain on the panel as it goes through a developing stage. This polymerized layer then acts as the barrier to the etching solution applied to the metal.

The actual methods of coating the metal with the photoresist are: dipping, spraying, flow coating, roller coating or, most recently, laminating. The type of resist used and the part's physical form will determine which method is most applicable.

**Fig. 4–27.**  Parts produced by chemical blanking. *(Courtesy, Chemcut Corporation)*

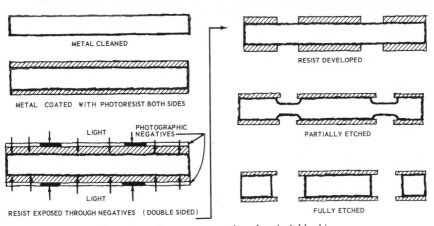

**Fig. 4–28.**  Process  steps  in  chemical blanking.

After coating with resist, it is generally necessary to bake the panel prior to exposing it. This "prebake," as it is called, is used to drive off solvents in a simple drying operation. Care must be taken not to overbake the photoresists since most of them are sensitive to heat prior to exposure.

Artwork that has been drawn and photographically reduced is used to expose the photographic resist. The negatives are generally used in matched pairs so that a minimum amount of undercut is achieved and so that the final part will have straight side walls. The metallic-coated panel is placed between sets of negatives (either film or glass) and clamped by either vacuum or pressure. The photoresists are generally sensitive to actinic light (2500 Angstroms to 5000 Angstroms) and are relatively insensitive to room light, with the exception of ordinary fluorescent lights. (Gold fluorescent lights are usually exceptions.) Exposure times depend upon light intensity, the type of resist being used, and the amount of sensitizers present in the resist. Typical exposure times of from 1.0 to 4 min. are required in currently used equipment.

The equipment used for printing ranges from very simple, single-sided graphic-arts-type vacuum frames (such as are used by photo-engravers) up to extremely complex automatic equipment for printing on continuous strips such as the one shown in Fig. 4-29. Fig. 4-30 shows a color television shadow mask produced on a similar line.

**Fig. 4–29.** Automatic equipment used to print photoresists on continuous strips for photochemically blanked parts. *(Courtesy, Chemcut Corporation)*

**Fig. 4–30.** Color television shadow mask produced by photochemical process. *(Courtesy, Chemcut Corporation)*

The exposed image can be developed by a number of process methods. Each photoresist has its own developing solution which may be water, alkaline solution, hydrocarbons, solvents, or proprietary developers. In most cases, the image is developed either by immersion followed by subsequent wash-off, or by spray equipment. Developing is always followed by a washing operation to ensure that no residual resist is left on the panels in the areas to be etched away.

Certain resists require an additional baking operation following development. This "postbake" is necessary to drive out residual solvents or cause further polymerization which improves the chemical resistance of the resist image. Postbaking is not as critical as the prebake in regard to time and temperature, but is generally tailored to the specific resist used and the depth of etch to be obtained. Either infrared lamps, conveyorized infrared ovens, or circulating air ovens are used for postbaking. In isolated instances, induction heating equipment has been used on ferrous materials. Following postbaking, it is generally advisable to cool the resist prior to etching.

The next step is etching to remove the unwanted metal unprotected by the photoresists. A large number of etchants are available for different materials. Many materials can be attacked by a number of etchants with the deciding factors being cost, quality, and speed of material removal. Table IV-1 lists etchants and a number of commonly-etched materials that they will attack.

The etchant may be applied to the workpiece by immersion, splash, or spray. Less commonly used techniques are air-driven mists or fogs, and gaseous medium etching. Fig. 4-31 shows a typical etching machine used for chemical blanking.

**Fig. 4–31.** Typical etching machine used for chemical blanking. *(Courtesy, Chemcut Corporation)*

Following etching, the workpiece is generally washed and dried if resist removal is not required. Where it is necessary to remove the resist, this can be accomplished either manually, or by machines which either spray on the removal compounds or use mechanical action in addition to chemical action.

### Screen Printing

Fig. 4-32 shows the steps involved when using a screen printed resist rather than a photographically printed resist. Most of the steps in this process are

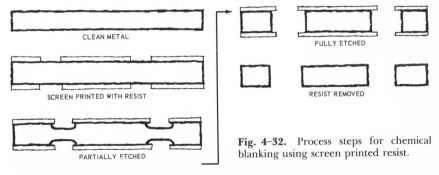

CLEAN METAL

FULLY ETCHED

SCREEN PRINTED WITH RESIST

RESIST REMOVED

PARTIALLY ETCHED

**Fig. 4–32.** Process steps for chemical blanking using screen printed resist.

identical to those in photochemical blanking. The metal is cleaned by one or more of the processes cited in the photochemical blanking steps. Cleaning for screen resists is generally not as critical as it is for photographic resists because the screen resists have better adhesion and their adhesion is less dependent upon the surface cleanliness of the material on which they are printed.

The clean panel is placed in either a manual or automatic screen printer and acid resistant ink is screened onto the part. Following printing, it is necessary to dry the resist and, quite often, it is necessary to print the reverse side of the panel if higher accuracy or thicker materials are to be chemically blanked.

After printing is complete and the acid resist has been properly dried or baked, the part is etched in the normal manner. Following etching, the screen resists are generally removed by either chemical action or a combination of chemical and mechanical action. Due to the inherent limitations of screen printing, high-tolerance work cannot be done with currently available screen printing equipment. However, the costs of screen printing are so much lower than the costs of photographic printing that, when tolerances permit, the former technique should be used. Generally, the cost of screen printing will be only 20 per cent of the cost for photographic printing on a per unit area basis.

## Tooling

The tooling required for chemical blanking consists of the artwork and negatives used to produce the acid resistant image. As with any product, the quality of the finished item depends upon the quality of the tooling.

**Artwork.** The actual artwork design depends on the final part desired and the process used to produce the part. The artwork for chemical blanking should be made on dimensionally stable materials such as Mylar, glass, or metallic-base materials. For best tolerances, scribing or strippable coatings should be used to take advantage of process capabilities. Less accurate work can be done with normal drafting techniques using a true black ink on a stabilized Mylar drawing film.

*Tolerances.* Since artwork is generally drawn oversize, the tolerances that can be held on a particular part depend to a great extent on the size of the part. Tighter tolerances can be held on smaller parts that can be drawn many times oversize and then photographically reduced, than can be held on larger parts which can be drawn only a few times oversize. A good draftsman with proper equipment can work to a tolerance of .002 to .003 in. over a 20 in. area. Where a drawing of such size can be reduced 20:1, tolerances within ±.00025 in. are achievable. Larger parts and smaller reduction ratios would necessarily result in lower overall accuracies of the negatives.

Some tolerance is lost during the photographic reduction due to camera errors. These errors are mainly caused by lens distortion, film plane lens, and copyboard nonparallelism. Generally, the tightest tolerance can be held on 2 sq. in. or smaller. As parts increase in size, camera error will increase. Above a certain point, it is better to use high-accuracy drawing equipment such as coordinatographs, and work the artwork 1:1. With extreme care, it is possible to produce 1:1 artwork accurate to ±.0015 in. over large areas.

*Undercut.* As the etchant eats into the surface of the exposed metal, to a lesser extent it also etches away underneath the resist image. When the part is completely blanked through, there is a noticeable reduction in dimension from the acid resist image originally placed upon it. The term "undercut" has been applied to this phenomenon and is expressed as a ratio of the depth of cut to the amount of undercut and varies for different metals and methods of etching (see Fig. 4-33). An etch factor of 3:1 means that, for every .003 in. of etch depth, .001 in. of undercut will occur. If the etch factor for a particular metal and

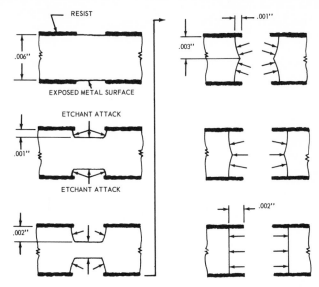

**Fig. 4-33.** Undercut.

etchant is known (see Table IV-1), then it can be used as a means for compensating the artwork by allowing for dimensional reduction so that accurately shaped parts can be produced.

Proper artwork compensation is one of the most important phases of chemical blanking because, without it, there is little hope of holding required tolerances. If, for instance, it has been determined that .002 in. of undercut will occur on a part to be etched from metal that is .006 in. thick, then the part OD at the artwork stage must be increased by .002 in. all around or, conversely, the ID must be decreased by the same amount.

Because of inherent undercut, there is a minimum size limit for slots, holes, and other piercings that can be produced by chemical blanking. Expressing the thickness of the sheet stock to be blanked as "$T$," the following blanking limitations on slots, holes, etc., are characteristic: .7$T$ for copper alloys; 1.0$T$ for steel alloys; and 1.4$T$ for aluminum alloys and stainless steel. Thus, the smallest hole that can be chemically pierced into .010 in. brass and still provide a near-vertical wall would be .007 in.

As a general rule, internal corners will develop radii equal to ±1.0 times the stock thickness. External corners can be held much sharper, generally equal to approximately $\frac{1}{3}$ the stock thickness. However, the addition of small fillets to the artwork is of great value in reducing radii in certain cases.

*Number of Parts.* Another point to be considered when designing the initial artwork for a chemically blanked part is the number of parts to be produced at one time. If the parts are small, it is beneficial to produce a large number of parts at one time, since the processing costs for a small panel are the same as the processing costs for a large panel (excluding materials, of course). Where a large number of parts are to be chemically blanked, it is desirable to have multiple images on the same film after photographic reduction. This is generally accomplished with automatic step and repeat machines which can take a single image and generate a large number of images very simply.

**Negatives.** Since most high-accuracy chemical blanking is done with acid resistant images on both the front and back sides of the metal, it is necessary to produce accurate matching inverse images on 2 sheets of film or glass plates so that double-sided printing can be accomplished. It is generally desirable to produce both images—the original and the mirror image—from a single master drawing so that accurate registration is assured. It is extremely difficult and needlessly expensive to try to generate two identical patterns in mirror image shapes by mechanical methods; the photographic methods for producing such images are well established. After the 2 images have been generated, it is necessary to register them accurately, one relative to the other, so that the images on the metal are in proper register. With extremely thin materials, registration may be accomplished by taping the film transparencies together, or by gluing glass negatives together with contact cement. With thicker materials, however, registration must be accomplished by either dowel pins or edge locating fixtures combined with negative clamps. In any case, it is advisable to put location marks on the negatives since it is difficult to use the actual part patterns to register the images accurately.

**Miscellaneous Tooling.** Further tooling considerations involve the method in which the parts are held in the sheet during chemical blanking. The three common methods are: dropping out, tabbing, and back-coating. While all of these methods are acceptable procedures for part retention, each has its advantages and limitations.

*Drop-Out.* This method is, of course, limited to equipment designed to catch or reclaim parts that have been completely blanked out. The artwork used in this method should be designed so that an opaque border will completely surround the part on subsequent negatives. Etching then occurs on all areas around the part and, hence, the part will "drop-out" onto a screen for subsequent overetching. Fig. 4-34 shows parts etched in this manner.

The major advantage of the drop-out method is that parts are ready for use immediately after resist removal. This is advantageous for larger parts, but where several thousand small parts are involved, it creates quite a handling problem.

*Tabbing.* When using this method, small connectors or "tabs" are added to the artwork in such a manner as to tie all parts together in the final sheet as shown in Fig. 4-35. From a processing point of view, the tabbing method has the major advantages of handling ease and one-step etching in high-speed, conveyorized systems. However, the one major disadvantage is the subsequent cutting and finishing operations necessitated by the use of tabs.

*Back-Coating.* There are several ways to hold the artwork together in the "back-coating" method, most notably spray coating and taping. (The artwork design is the same as that used in the "drop-out" method.) In the back-coating method, etching generally proceeds to the point where breakthrough will occur very soon. At that point, the blank is withdrawn, rinsed, and allowed to dry.

**Fig. 4-34.** "Drop-out" etching. *(Courtesy, Chemcut Corporation)*

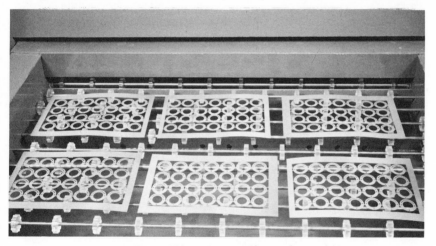

**Fig. 4-35.** Tabbing. *(Courtesy, Chemcut Corporation)*

The back-coating is then applied to one etched surface and etching proceeds from one side only. The parts are also over-etched on the backing to obtain vertical edges. Fig. 4-36 shows taped backed-coated parts emerging from final etching.

The back-coating method lends itself to automatic conveyorized etching but has the disadvantage of creating more process steps. It would seem, therefore, that this method would be more time-consuming and it is. But experience has shown that back-coating is more advantageous than either of the other two methods described above for processing large quantities of small parts. The parts can be removed either by hand when ready for use, or the backing can be dissolved and the parts freed.

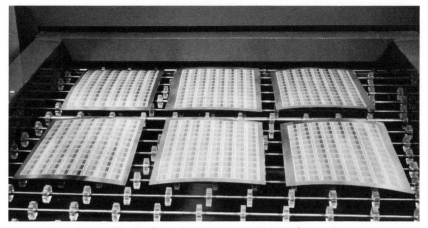

**Fig. 4–36.** Back-coating. *(Courtesy, Chemcut Corporation)*

## Applications

The use of chemical blanking is generally limited to relatively thin materials, from .0001 to .030 in. thick. The limit on material thickness is generally a function of the tolerance desired on finished parts. Table IV-3 shows typical

**Table IV-3. Representative Tolerances for Chemically Blanked Parts Not Exceeding 2 by 2 in.**

| Material | Thickness (in.) | | | | | |
|---|---|---|---|---|---|---|
| | .002 | .005 | .010 | .020 | .040 | .060 |
| Aluminum alloys | ±.0003 | ±.0007 | ±.0015 | ±.003 | ±.005 | ±.007 |
| Copper and its alloys | ±.0002 | ±.0005 | ±.001 | ±.002 | ±.004 | ±.006 |
| Nickel | ±.0002 | ±.0005 | ±.001 | ±.002 | ±.005 | ±.008 |
| Steel alloys | ±.0002 | ±.0005 | ±.001 | ±.002 | ±.005 | ±.007 |
| Stainless steel | ±.0005 | ±.001 | ±.002 | ±.004 | ±.008 | ±.012 |

tolerances which can be achieved by chemical blanking on various common materials. The factors which affect tolerance are: (1) accuracy of initial artwork, (2) accuracy of photographic processing, (3) compensation of artwork for undercut, and (4) nonuniformities in processing such as nonuniform printing, developing, and etching.

Chemical blanking has a number of applications wherein it provides unique advantages. Some of these include:

1) Working on extremely thin materials where handling difficulties and die accuracies preclude the use of normal mechanical methods.

2) Working on hardened or brittle materials where mechanical action would cause breakage or stress concentration points. Chemical blanking works well on spring materials and hardened materials which are relatively difficult to punch.
3) Production of parts which must be absolutely burr-free. Chemical blanking inherently produces a burr-free part, and edge contour can be shaped from concave to convex, depending upon the processing used.
4) Production of extremely complex parts where die costs would be prohibitive.
5) Producing short-run parts where the relatively low setup costs and short time from print to production offer advantages. This is especially important in research and development projects and in model shops.

# ELECTRIC DISCHARGE MACHINING

Of the non-traditional machining processes described in this book, electric discharge machining (EDM) is, undoubtedly, the most widely used in production, as well as in the tool-rooms of both in-house and supplier job shops. Chapter 1, which discusses all of the non-traditional machining processes in relation to each other, points out that unmachinable metals and metal heat-treated to an unmachinable condition can be processed by EDM with good dimensional control. Chapter 1 also states that EDM is applicable only to metals and alloys, and has no application in the non-metallics such as ceramics, plastics, and glass.

## PROCESS PRINCIPLES

In the EDM process, material is removed by a series of discrete electrical discharges (sparks) that occur in the machining gap between the electrode and the workpiece. (The basic EDM system and mechanics of metal removal are illustrated in Figs. 5-1 and 5-2.) The dielectric fluid creates a path for the discharge as the fluid becomes ionized between the two closest points. The initiation of the discharge occurs when sufficient voltage is applied across the machining gap to cause the dielectric to ionize and current to start to flow. The tendency for the discharge to be initiated is increased if: the spacing between the electrode and the workpiece is reduced, the applied voltage is increased, or debris from previous discharges is suspended in the dielectric. The energy of the discharge

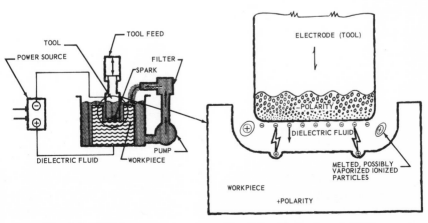

**Fig. 5-1.** EDM system.    **Fig. 5-2.** Mechanics of EDM process.

vaporizes and decomposes the dielectric surrounding the column of electrical conduction.

As conduction continues, the diameter of the discharge column expands and the current increases. The small area in which the discharge occurs is heated to an extremely high temperature so that a small portion of the workpiece material is elevated above its melting temperature and is removed.

With the high temperatures involved, it makes no difference whether the workpiece material has been heat-treated or not. The discharge temperature is high enough to machine the hardest and toughest of known metals, including the exotic metals.

## PROCESS PARAMETERS

**Discharge**

The size of the crater produced in the workpiece by the discharge is determined by the size of the discharge or, more accurately, the *energy* of the discharge. The energy of the discharge is determined by the gap voltage during discharge, the discharge current, and length of time that the current flows:

$$W = \frac{1}{2} EIt \tag{1}$$

Where: $W$ = Discharge energy
$E$ = Voltage
$I$ = Current
$t$ = Time

The amount of current is more important than the length of time. It has been observed that, if the discharge current is doubled and the conduction time is reduced by $\frac{1}{2}$, the metal removed by the discharge increases, even though the energy of the discharge is the same. Fig. 5-3 illustrates the energy and volume conditions. The discharge voltage (the voltage across the machin-

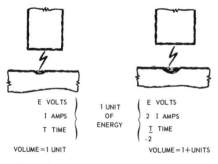

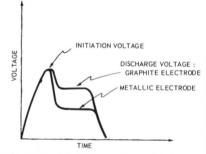

**Fig. 5-3.** Discharge energy and time as related to volume of metal removed.

**Fig. 5-4.** Discharge voltages for graphite electrodes are higher than for metallic electrodes.

ing gap while the discharge current is flowing) is not equal to the initiation voltage but is generally considerably lower (see Fig. 5-4). When the gap resistance breaks down, the voltage immediately drops from the initiation voltage level to discharge voltage level, which is a value independent of the current through the gap or the gap spacing and is determined only by the dielectric, and workpiece and electrode materials. (The operator has little choice in controlling the discharge voltage.) No great difference in discharge voltages is noticed except when graphite electrodes are used. In this case, the discharge voltage is approximately 1.5 times the voltage observed when metallic electrodes are used.

The discharge current is determined by the EDM power supply ratings and limitations. The highest possible current would be optimum for all machining conditions; however, the rate of rise and fall of the current at the beginning and end of the discharge (see Fig. 5-5) is determined by circuit inductance and other

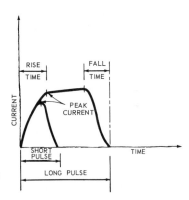

**Fig. 5-5.** Optimum currents cannot be obtained with short pulses.

considerations. The highest currents cannot be achieved when discharge times are short, as shown in Fig. 5-5. In many cases, the maximum discharge current is intentionally controlled to protect the power supply. The current flow can also be manually reduced to achieve specific machining conditions. This adjustment is normally called removal rate selector, or peak current control.

The length of time that the discharge continues is controlled directly by the power supply which the operator usually can control. This adjustment is called duty cycle, current control, removal rate control, or pulse width.

### Capacitance

When a capacitor is used as a storage element in the power supply, the capacitance (measured in microfarads), along with the inductance of the circuit connecting the capacitor to the machining gap, determine both the peak current and the discharge time. Increasing the capacitance causes the discharge energy to increase, and increases both the peak current and the discharge time:

$$W = \frac{1}{2} CE^2 = \frac{1}{2} EIt \qquad (2)$$

Where: $C$ = Capacitance
$E, I$, and $t$ are the same as in Eq. (1)

Reducing the circuit inductance but not changing the energy of the discharge makes metal removal more efficient by increasing the peak current and, simultaneously, reducing the discharge time as shown in Fig. 5-6. To obtain maximum efficiency, the inductance of the discharge circuit must be kept as low as possible. This is accomplished by keeping the two leads that connect to the electrode and the workpiece as close together as possible. Should a piece of iron or steel be allowed to lodge between the leads, it would increase the inductance of the circuit and reduce the machining rate. It is equally important to keep the inductance as low as possible on circuits that do not use energy stor-

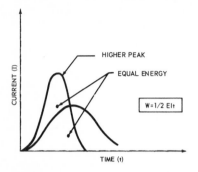

**Fig. 5-6.** With equal energy, the shorter time and higher pulse current created by lower inductance results in greater metal removal.

age means (capacitance) since, in any case, the inductance will cause a slower rise and fall of the machining current.

## Dielectric Fluid

The dielectric fluid is an important variable in the EDM process. It has three main functions: (1) as an insulator between tool and work, (2) as a coolant, and (3) as a flushing medium for chip removal. It also has an important effect on electrode wear, metal removal rate, and other EDM characteristics.

Although fluids used for EDM have traditionally been oils such as kerosene, transformer oils, and various other petroleum distillate fractions (50-Viscosity S.S.U. being the most common), U.S. Air Force investigations (1) have shown that, when used with *metallic* electrodes, the hydrocarbon fluids do not break down easily enough to assure the formation of an electrical discharge after each charging pulse. Significantly increased machining rates, reduced tool wear, and better discharge initiation and stability can be obtained only by the use of metallic electrodes and improved fluids, e.g., triethylene glycol plus water. A comparison among various fluids is made in Table V-1. The study also found that metallic

**Table V-1. Comparison of Dielectric Fluids for Brass Electrodes and Tool Steel Workpieces**

| EDM Fluid | Machining Rate | W/T Ratio |
|---|---|---|
| 50 viscosity S.S.U. hydrocarbon oil | 2.5 | 2.8 |
| Distilled water | 3.5 | 2.7 |
| Tap water (typical) | 3.7 | 4.1 |
| Triethylene glycol   $H_2O$ (40)* | 6.6 | 6.8 |
| Tetraethylene glycol   $H_2O$ (30)* | 4.3 | 11.3** |

$$\text{Machining Rate} = \frac{in^3 \text{ work removed} \times 10^4}{amp\text{-}min}$$

$$\text{W/T Ratio} = \frac{\text{Volume work removed}}{\text{Volume tool removed}}$$

*Volume of $H_2O$     **90 microfarad

electrode wear could be reduced by at least 50 per cent through the use of chemical scavengers in the fluid, and by the formation of thin oxide films on the electrode surfaces in the presence of fluids which are aqueous mixtures of polar organic compounds.

### Deionization

When the discharge is completed, the voltage across the machining gap is held to a low value while waiting for the dielectric fluid to deionize. As shown in Fig. 5-7, the voltage must be kept below the value of the discharge voltage until deionization is complete, or current will immediately start to flow through

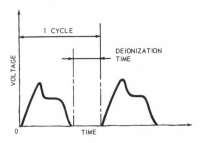

**Fig. 5–7.** Deionization of gap.

the gap at the location of the preceding discharge. The time it takes for deionization to become complete depends upon the energy contained in the previous discharge; the larger the energy, the longer the time it will take for the gap to recover.

### Frequency

Two time elements are required to complete the machining cycle: the discharge time and the waiting time. The sum of these times determines the cycle time and, therefore, determines the frequency or how many discharges of a particular size can take place each second. As illustrated in Fig. 5-8, increased discharge frequency can improve the surface finish.

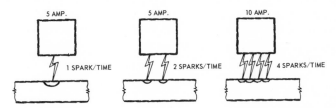

**Fig. 5–8.** Effect of current and frequency on surface finish and metal removal rate.

At a hypothetical frequency of 2 sparks/sec at 5 amp., energy is divided between 2 sparks, each taking a smaller chip than the single 5 amp. spark. Within limits, by doubling the amperage and frequency, the metal removal rate will double without changing the finish. At high frequencies, the amperage is reduced due to inductance, thereby reducing the metal removal rate. The economics involved, therefore, set a practical limit on surface finish. The relationship between current and frequency on surface finish is shown in Fig. 5-9.

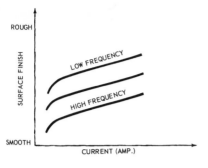

**Fig. 5–9.** Surface finish as related to frequency and current.

## Overcut

The overcut is that distance by which the machined hole in the workpiece exceeds the electrode size (see Fig. 5-10), and is determined by both the initiating voltage and the discharge energy. It is equal to the length of the sparks that are discharged. As the discharge energy *(W)* is increased by higher current

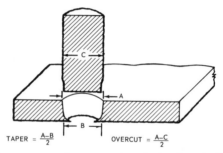

$$TAPER = \frac{A-B}{2} \qquad OVERCUT = \frac{A-C}{2}$$

**Fig. 5–10.** Values for overcut and taper can be calculated, and will vary with the materials and cutting conditions used.

*(I)*, the overcut increases. The relationship among current, frequency, and overcut is shown schematically in Fig. 5-11. The discharge energy can also be affected by capacitors and, in turn, influence the overcut. The overcut can be controlled,

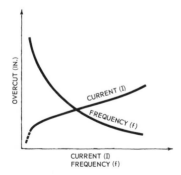

**Fig. 5–11.** Relationship of frequency and current to overcut.

therefore, by the initiating voltage and the discharge energy (which is a function of either the current or capacitance), whichever is the predominant factor in a particular machining situation.

The chart in Fig. 5-12 is based on a 40 amp., pulse-type power supply and can be used as a guide for cutting tool steel with copper-tungsten electrodes.

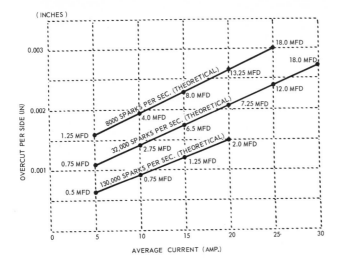

**Fig. 5–12.** Overcut chart is used as a guide when cutting tool steel with copper tungsten. The chart is accurate within .0002 in.

## Metal Removal Rate

The metal removal rate (MRR) depends upon the volume of metal removed by each spark and by the frequency of discharge. The volume of metal removed per discharge is a function of the discharge energy which, in turn, is increased by increasing the current ($W = \frac{1}{2} EIt$).

Since the metal particles are removed mainly by heat in EDM, the volume of metal removed also varies with the melting point of the workpiece. The following relationships have been established empirically (1):

$$Rw = 2.43 \, Mw^{-1.23} \tag{3}$$

$$V = 1.36 \times 10^{-4} \, Mw^{-1.43} \tag{4}$$

Where:  $Rw$ = Average metal removal rate from workpiece (in³/amp -min × 10⁴)

$Mw$ = Melting point of workpiece (°C.)

$V$ = Average volume/discharge (in³)

Capacitance also affects the amount of metal removed per discharge because the electrical energy is generally stored in a capacitor. More capacitance is needed as amperage goes up, but there is a point at which capacitance has an adverse effect on machining. Too much capacitance will decrease discharge stability (ratio of actual number of discharges across the gap to the theoretical or possible discharges per unit time), as illustrated in Fig. 5-13.

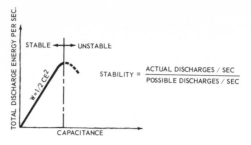

**Fig. 5–13.** Effect of capacitance on stability.

## Heat Affected Zone

The EDM process is a thermal process and, therefore, some annealing of the workpiece can be expected in a zone just below the machined surface. This effect can be minimized by machining at lower rates, i.e., using a finish cut to remove the annealed material left by the previous high-speed roughing cut. In addition, not all of the workpiece material melted by the discharge is expelled into the dielectric. The remaining melted material is quickly chilled, primarily by heat conduction into the bulk of the workpiece, resulting in an exceedingly hard surface. The annealing effect is most common when unstable machining conditions exist and can be reduced by choosing electrodes that produce more stable machining.

The surface condition resulting from EDM, therefore, consists of 2 distinct layers. In hardened steel, the outer layer of metal is extremely hard (68 to 70 Rockwell C) and shallow. Its depth ranges from .0001 in. for fine finish machining to approximately .0005 in. for roughing cuts. Directly below the hard surface is a second layer of metal that is slightly annealed. The depth of the annealed layer is also proportional to the amount of power used in the cutting operation. It will range from .002 in. for finish cutting, to approximately .008 in. for high metal removal rates. The amount of annealing is usually about 2 points of hardness below the parent metal for finish cutting. In the roughing cuts, the annealing effect is approximately 5 points of hardness below the parent metal. Fig. 5-14 shows the relationship of the heat affected zone to the cutting conditions.

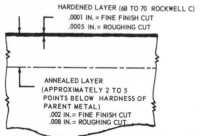

**Fig. 5–14.** EDM heat affected zone.

Intragranular attack has been noticed following EDM on high-melting-point heterogeneous alloy workpieces such as the iron-based Superalloy A-286. This is caused by the fact that the composition of the material is different at the grain boundary than in the grain itself.

Not all workpiece materials are subject to heat effects but, when they are, these effects can be minimized by machining at lower rates and under conditions that produce good stability.

## Electrode Wear

As previously pointed out, the size of the crater produced in the workpiece is determined by the energy of the discharge and the workpiece material. Some of the discharge energy is applied to the electrode and, thus, a crater is also produced in the electrode which is likewise dependent on the electrode material and the energy of the discharge. Materials having good electrode wear characteristics are the same as those that are difficult to machine. These are materials that require large amounts of energy to melt a given volume and usually have high melting temperatures. One of the principal materials used for electrodes is graphite which does not melt, but goes directly to the vapor phase. The vaporization for a given particle size requires a greater amount of energy than the melting of a similar particle of a metallic electrode and accounts for the favorable wear characteristics of graphite.

The following relationships for metallic electrode (tool) wear have been established (1):

$$R_t = 6.51 \times 10^2 \, M_T^{-2.28} \tag{5}$$

Where:  $R_t$ = Average metal removal rate from electrode (in³/amp-min × 10⁴)

   $M_T$ = Melting point of electrode (°C.)

$$W_R = 2.25 \, M_R^{-2.3} \tag{6}$$

Where:  $W_R$ = Wear ratio (work/tool)

   $M_R$ = Melting point ratio (work/tool)

## Summary

In EDM, surface roughness, overcut, and metal removal rate can be controlled using voltage, current, frequency, and capacity. The following approximate relations hold: surface roughness is a function of the current divided by the frequency; overcut is determined by the voltage and discharge energy; and metal removal rate is determined by the current (see Table V-2).

## POWER SUPPLY CIRCUITS

Several basic types of electrical circuits, illustrated in Fig. 5-15, are available to provide pulsating DC to electrical discharge machines. No one particular type is suitable for all machining conditions; some of the advantages and disadvantages of the systems are given in Table V-3.

**Table V-2. EDM Variables**

| Independent Variables | Dependent Variables |
|---|---|
| Surface Roughness (SR)<br>Overcut (OC)<br>Metal Removal Rate (MRR) | Voltage $(E)$<br>Current$(I)$<br>Frequency $(f)$<br>Capacitance $(C)$ |
| **Basic Energy Equation** | **Primary Relationships** |
| $W = \frac{1}{2}\,EIt = \frac{1}{2}\,CE^2$<br>$W$ = discharge energy<br>$t$ = cycle time | SR $\approx I/f$<br>OC $\approx (W, E)$<br>MRR $\approx (I)$ |

**Table V-3. Advantages and Disadvantages of Various Power Supply Circuits**

| Type | Advantages | Disadvantages |
|---|---|---|
| Basic | Simple, low cost | Low frequency, rough surface at higher metal removal rates (MRR) |
| Resistance-Capitance (RC) | Simple, rugged, reliable, higher frequencies, low cost | Relatively low machining rates for smooth surfaces |
| Rotary impulse generator (RIG) | Capable of high metal removal rates | Rough surfaces |
| Controlled pulse-vacuum tube | High frequency controls eliminate short circuit, good metal removal rates, improved electrode wear | Characteristics of vacuum tube and gap not compatible:<br>Arc gap = high current<br>    = low voltage<br>Vacuum tube = high voltage<br>    = low current<br>Must use auxiliary power source or transformer to compensate |
| Controlled pulse-transistor | (Same as vacuum tube) plus higher efficiency due to compatibility with arc gap. | |

Several early EDM power supplies were somewhat sophisticated versions of the one shown in Fig. 5-15$A$. In this basic circuit, with switch (S) in position (1), the DC source (E) charges capacitor (C). Movement of switch (S) to position (2) connects the charged capacitor across the gap; if the electrode and tool are in a suitably close mechanical relation, the capacitor will discharge through the gap and the spark will remove a minute amount of workpiece material. The metal removed per discharge, the surface finish produced, and the "overcut" or gap clearance between tool and workpiece, are parameters directly dependent upon the capacitor. This gap capacity ranges from .01 to 100 microfarads during normal usage.

The principal objection to this basic circuit is the mechanical problem of

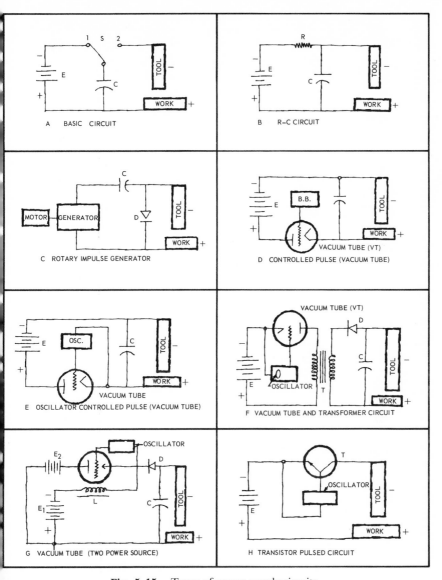

**Fig. 5–15.** Types of power supply circuits.

operating switch (S) at sufficiently high speeds to obtain the desired frequencies. This problem is solved by the circuit shown in Fig. 5-15*B* where resistor (R) accomplishes the switching function. Capacitor (C) is charged by source (E) through resistor (R). When the voltage across (C) becomes sufficiently high, capacitor (C) abruptly discharges through the gap, and the cycle repeats. The basic characteristics of this type of circuit dictate the use of copper as the primary electrode material. This circuit is variously known as an "R-C Circuit" (because of R and C); as a "Relaxation Oscillator"; and as the "Russian Circuit" (because it was first used by two Russian investigators, B. R. and N. I. Lazarenko in 1943).

While the relaxation oscillator is highly desirable in that it is simple and rugged, it is severely limited in metal removal capability. The gap current is increased by varying the parameters (E), (C), and (R); however, for gap currents greater than 4 or 5 amp., the circuit becomes unstable and erratic in operation. What is known as "DC arcing" occurs and, as the term implies, the workpiece is scorched and burned.

As an interesting example of "discovery" and "rediscovery," B. Kohlschutter used this identical circuit in Germany, in 1919, to prepare colloidal suspensions for scientific study. Although Kohlschutter's work was reported in great detail in the scientific journals at the time, the practical value of the circuit went unappreciated because Kohlschutter was only interested in the fine "chips" produced by EDM. He actually threw the "workpiece" away. Today, of course, the interest is in the machined piece and the "chips" are thrown away in the form of sludge.

Until very recently, most of the commercially available EDM power supplies were simply variations of Fig. 5-15B with almost no modifications. This circuit is still used extensively throughout the world outside of the United States.

### Rotary Impulse Generators

In searching for a means to increase metal removal rates, motor generators were developed to supply the required machining power. Various means were used to produce an asymmetric output wave so that the advantage of the equivalent of a DC power supply could be maintained. These generators are commonly referred to as rotary impulse generators, (RIG). The basic circuitry of one RIG is illustrated in Fig. 5-15C. In operation, the capacitor (C) is charged through the diode (D) on $1/2$ cycle. On the following $1/2$ cycle, the sum of the voltage from the generator, plus the voltage on the charged capacitor, is applied to the gap. This circuit allows a standard high frequency AC generator to be used to produce unidirectional pulses.

The RIG is capable of removing metal at very high rates but, in so doing, produces an exceedingly rough surface finish. The operating frequency is necessarily low and is not adjustable, thus making better surface finishes impossible.

### Switching

In all of the circuits discussed above, the switching device was the primary factor in determining both the frequency of the gap discharge and the amount of energy in each discharge. One element of control lacking in these basic circuits is the ability to stop the current flow in case a short-circuit develops at the gap. One method of breaking a short-circuit in both the RIG and the basic circuits is to mechanically remove the electrode from the work. However, the withdrawal of the electrode requires so much time that objectionable burning or melting takes place.

### Controlled Pulse Circuits

Therefore, the need for a fast and positive means to electronically stop the current flow resulted in the development of circuits in which vacuum tubes or transistors are used as the switching devices. These circuits are known as controlled pulse circuits (CPC). In circuits employing electronic switching, CPC also provide the added benefits of faster metal removal and improved electrode wear.

The development of circuits incorporating vacuum tubes preceded that of transistors. In the early vacuum tube circuits, the resistor (R) indicated in Fig. 5-15B was replaced with a number of vacuum tubes connected in parallel (shown as a single tube (VT) in Fig. 5-15D). Properly controlled, the tube bank becomes, in effect, a variable resistor.

The grids of the tube bank (VT) serve, therefore, as the switching device. The grids are connected to an electronic control circuit (BB) which turns on the tubes in order to charge the capacitor (C) and also provides the means to stop the current flow in case a short-circuit develops at the gap.

The current that flows in the gap comes from the capacitor. If any current flows in the gap, the tubes are "turned off" or "biased to cut off." When this occurs, the tubes cannot pass much current and, therefore, appear as high resistance (1,000 ohms or higher) to the rest of the circuit. When current ceases to flow in the gap, the control (BB) reduces the grid bias. The tubes become highly conductive (low in resistance), and capacitor (C) is charged rapidly in preparation for the following gap discharge.

The circuit just described was the first of the broadly-defined class of "pulsed" EDM power supplies. The pulsed circuit resulted in a substantial increase in metal removal and also allowed the use of brass as an electrode material.

Eventually, it was learned that the circuit could be simplified and operating stability improved by replacing the control (BB) with a simple switching device in the form of a fixed-frequency oscillator as shown in Fig. 5-15E. In other words, it was not necessary for the tube grid control to be associated with the arc gap except for current cutoff in case of a short-circuit at the gap. It was only necessary to insure that the gap current was periodically interrupted by the switching device at a sufficiently high cyclic rate.

Growing awareness of the usefulness of EDM led, inevitably, to the demand for higher metal removal capability. Since the metal removal rate is substantially proportional to average gap amperage, higher current power supplies, if made in this form, require large numbers of vacuum tubes.

The electrical characteristics of vacuum tubes and an arc gap are not directly compatible. In fact, the arc gap will pass high currents at relatively low voltages, while vacuum tubes are inherently high-voltage, low-current devices.

Therefore, 3 types of circuits were developed to achieve higher metal removal rates and solve the problem of incompatibility between gap and vacuum tube characteristics. These circuits:

1) Use a small number of vacuum tubes on the primary side of a transformer where they can operate very efficiently at high voltages and low currents. The gap is then connected to the secondary side where a low-voltage and high-current condition is obtainable.

2) Use a tube-type power supply and augment its output with an auxiliary power source.

3) Replace the tubes of a simple pulsed circuit with transistors which can function at high efficiencies at the normal gap conditions of low voltages and high currents.

Fig. 5-15*F* shows a simplified circuit using vacuum tubes and a transformer. Since a transformer supplied with a pulsating DC from the vacuum tubes will emit AC on the secondary, a diode (D) is used to assure a constant polarity at the gap.

Although the schematic arrangement is highly desirable, in that it permits a substantial reduction in the number of vacuum tubes required, the use of the transformer imposes a limitation at high frequencies.

Fig. 5-15*G* shows an increased power circuit which is a combination of a tube-type power supply and an integral secondary power source. The tube-pulsed portion of the circuit is used as the switching device to determine the frequency, but the combination of the 2 power sources determines the current flow at the gap.

The most recent solution to the problem of obtaining increased metal removal without using a large bank of vacuum tubes as the switching device, is to employ transistors which can function at low voltages and high currents. Fig. 5-15*H*, which is similar to Fig. 5-15*E*, illustrates schematically the use of transistors to replace vacuum tubes. In this circuit, the switching is driven by an oscillator at selected imposed frequency; but it does not require the use of capacitors in parallel with the gap. The oscillator is also controlled by the gap conditions so that the transistors can be turned off in case of a DC short-circuit at the gap.

## MACHINE TOOL DESIGN

EDM equipment manufacturers offer a variety of machine tools ranging from small machines to massive units. Machine types are designed for application requirements as shown in Table V-4 which relates the type of EDM machines, the field of application, and the size range of tooling processed in that field for particular types of machines.

Many characteristics of EDM machines are unique to and dictated by the process, as well as the nature of the workpiece. The factors to be considered in selecting any one machine are: (1) number of parts to be produced, (2) accuracy required, (3) size of the workpiece, (4) size of the electrode, (5) depth of the cavity, and (6) orientation of the cavity.

### Number of Parts to be Produced

For tool room EDM work, where job lot quantities are produced and a great variety of workpiece configurations is encountered, equipment must be versatile, accurate, and may require optional accessories such as rotating spindles, optics, table servos, etc. Typically, general purpose tool room machines fall into three catagories: (1) bed type, quill head as shown in Fig. 5-16, (2) bed type, ram head as shown in Fig. 5-17, and (3) knee type, quill head as shown in Fig. 5-18. The construction of these machines is similar to that of vertical milling machines with the cutting tool (electrode) usually attached to the head of the machine by a holder. The electrode holders normally used are vee blocks, collet chucks, and

**Fig. 5–16.** Bed-type, quill head machine. *(Courtesy, The Ingersoll Milling Machine Company)*

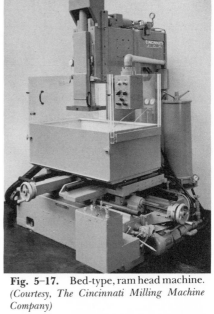

**Fig. 5–17.** Bed-type, ram head machine. *(Courtesy, The Cincinnati Milling Machine Company)*

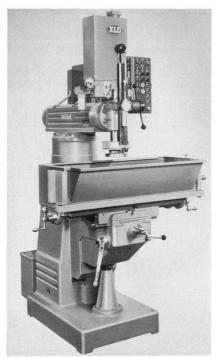

**Fig. 5–18.** Knee-type, quill head machine. *(Courtesy, The Ex-Cell-O Corporation)*

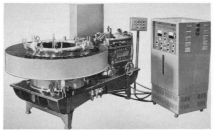

**Fig. 5–19.** Horizontally actuated machine. *(Courtesy, The Ingersoll Milling Machine Company)*

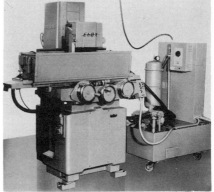

**Fig. 5–20.** EDM grinder. *(Courtesy, Elox Corporation of Michigan)*

### Table V-4. Applications Guide to EDM Machine Selection

| | Stamping Dies | Molds and Die-Cast Dies | Forging Dies |
|---|---|---|---|
| STYLE OF EDM MACHINE | • General uniform die-clearance for all cutting dies including blanking, trimming, contour trimming, notching, lancing, piercing, and perforating.<br>• Electrically "shear-in" hardened punch into hardened die.<br>• Produce interchangeable die details, reduce sectionalizing, perform engineering changes and rework, simplify die maintenance, simplify die repair, reduce die engineering, eliminate heat-treat hazards, produce stronger solid punch clusters, reduce die fit-up, reduce the amount of stock removal for sharpening. | • Produce cavities, cores, ribbing, intricate detail, gusseting, parting line matching, core shut-off, sub-gating, texturing.<br>• Reduce inserting.<br>• Simplify and improve water-line design. | • Cavity sinking, re-sinking.<br>• Hot trim dies, cold trim dies.<br>• Contouring of trim punching. |
| Knee | *Small and Medium Dies for:*<br>Fasteners<br>General Hardware<br>Cutlery<br>Motor Laminations<br>Jewelry<br>Photographic Equipment | *Small and Medium Molds and Dies for:*<br>Electronic Components<br>Toys and Hobby Kits<br>Knobs • Gears • Cams<br>Novelties • Packaging<br>Rubber Products<br>Instruments | *Small Dies and Inserts for:*<br>General Hardware<br>Marine Fittings<br>Hydraulic Fittings<br>Hand Tools<br>Pull-Line Hardware |
| Bed Quill and Slide | *Small and Medium Dies for:*<br>Fasteners • General Hardware<br>Cutlery • Motor Laminations<br>Jewelry • Photographic Equipment • Small Appliances •<br>Gears | *Small and Medium Molds and Dies for:*<br>Electronic Components<br>Toys and Hobby Kits<br>Knobs • Gears • Cams<br>Novelties • Packaging<br>Rubber Products<br>Instruments | *Small Dies and Inserts for:*<br>General Hardware<br>Marine Fittings<br>Hydraulic Fittings<br>Hand Tools<br>Pull-Line Hardware |
| Bed Ram and Bed Ram and Slide | *Medium-Size Dies for:*<br>General Hardware<br>Small Appliances<br>Radio Chassis<br>Motor Laminations<br>Business Machine Parts | *Medium-Size Molds and Dies for:*<br>Household Appliances<br>Electrical Components<br>Cabinets • Novelties<br>Photographic Equipment<br>Toys and Hobby Kits<br>Cases and Packaging | *Medium-Size Dies for:*<br>Automotive Engine Parts<br>Transmission Parts<br>Turbine Engine Parts<br>Small Farm Implements<br>Pull-Line Hardware<br>General and Marine Hardware<br>Hand Tools |
| Large Bed Ram | *Medium — Large Dies for:*<br>Appliances<br>Control Panels<br>Radio Chassis<br>Farm Implements<br>Large Motor Laminations<br>Radiators<br>Large General Hardware | *Medium — Large Molds and Dies for:*<br>Automotive Parts<br>Appliances • Cabinets<br>Panels • Grilles<br>Large Hardware<br>Large Toys and Models<br>Musical Instruments | *Medium — Large Dies for:*<br>Automotive Forgings<br>Farm Implements<br>Off-the-Road Equipment<br>Aircraft Landing Gear<br>Aircraft Engine Parts<br>Turbine Engines and<br>Propellers |
| Extra Large Bed Ram | *Medium — Large Dies for:*<br>Appliances<br>Farm Implements<br>Medium Automotive<br>Large Chassis<br>Large Control Panels<br>Aircraft Parts | *Medium — Large and Large Molds and Dies for:*<br>Automotive Parts and Grilles<br>Instrument Panels<br>Appliance Cabinets<br>Furniture<br>Aircraft Parts<br>Farm Machinery | *Large Dies for:*<br>Crankshafts<br>Aircraft Landing Gear<br>Large Connecting Rods<br>Torsion Bars<br>Farm Implements<br>Off-the-Road Equipment |
| 4 Column | *Large Dies for:*<br>Automotive Body Skins<br>Automotive Inner Liners<br>Automotive Pillars<br>Automotive Frames<br>Large Appliance Parts<br>Large Aircraft Panels<br>Large Farm Implement Panels | *Large Molds and Dies for:*<br>Automotive Panels<br>Automotive Grills<br>Large Appliances<br>Boats | |
| Press Conversion | *Large Dies for:*<br>Automotive Body Skins<br>Automotive Inner Liners<br>Automotive Pillars<br>Automotive Frames<br>Large Appliance Parts<br>Large Aircraft Panels<br>Large Farm Implement Panels | | |

## Table V-4. Applications Guide to EDM Machine Selection *(Cont'd.)*

| *Extrusion Dies* | *Header Dies* | *Compacting Dies* | *Production Work* |
|---|---|---|---|
| • Produce multiple identical openings.<br>• Reduce polishing.<br>• Simultaneous machining of mandrel and die openings on bridge dies.<br>• Reduce setup time on extrusion press.<br>• Produce identical repeat dies. | • Open-up washed-out dies to the next size.<br>• Machine carbide and harder steels.<br>• Machine special shapes for cavities.<br>• Machine hammer details.<br>• Re-size wire and rod draw dies. | • Produce solid dies for irregular shapes.<br>• Provide slots and holes for core pins (both regular and irregular shapes).<br>• Use standard nibs instead of waiting for presintered shapes.<br>• Make core and cavity one-piece construction.<br>• Use the best die material to suit the job— not to suit the making of the tools. | • Machine the new, harder exotic metals.<br>• Burr-free machining.<br>• Produce minute cross-sectional shapes.<br>• Conserve precious metals by removing useable slugs.<br>• Improve product by mating EDM with other modern production methods, such as N/C, cast-to-size, and by mating with the latest metallurgical advancements. |
| Standard-size aluminum track<br>Small structural shapes<br>Regular and irregular shapes for:<br>Brass • Copper • Steel, etc.<br>Rubber products<br>Plastic products | *Dies for:*<br>Fasteners<br>Bolts<br>Nuts<br>Rivets<br>Screws | *Dies for:*<br>Pump parts<br>Gears • Cams • Knobs<br>Firearm parts<br>Business machine parts<br>Links, Levers | |
| Standard-size aluminum track<br>Small structural shapes<br>Regular and irregular shapes for:<br>Brass • Copper • Steel, etc.<br>Rubber products<br>Plastic products | *Dies for:*<br>Fasteners<br>Bolts<br>Nuts<br>Rivets<br>Screws | *Dies for:*<br>Pump parts<br>Gears • Cams • Knobs<br>Firearm parts<br>Business Machine parts<br>Links, Levers | |
| Standard-size aluminum track<br>Small structural shapes<br>Regular and irregular shapes for:<br>Brass • Copper • Steel, etc.<br>Rubber products<br>Plastic products | *Dies for:*<br>Fasteners<br>Bolts<br>Nuts<br>Rivets<br>Screws | *Dies for:*<br>Pump parts<br>Gears • Rotors • Cams<br>Knobs<br>Firearm parts<br>Business machine parts<br>Links, Levers | While all standard EDM machines and power supplies can be used for prototype and small-lot production work, large-volume production work frequently requires special considerations: |
| *Large Dies for:*<br>Structural Shapes<br>Aluminum Shapes<br>Truck Flooring<br>Aircraft Landing-Field Mats | | | 1) Mating specially-designed machines with standard power supply units |
| | | | 2) Mating specially-designed power supply units with standard machines |
| *Very Large Dies for:*<br>Structural Shapes<br>Airport Landing Mats<br>Truck Flooring | | | 3) Building-block assembly of standard machine and power supply components |

platens. However, the electrode does not travel along the vertical axis in all EDM machines. For example, the electrode may travel horizontally as shown in Fig. 5-19. Or the electrode may rotate while the workpiece travels as in an EDM grinder (see Fig. 5-20).

General purpose tool room machines may be used for production work, providing they incorporate high production tooling. The volume of production, however, may warrant designing a single purpose machine tool.

### Accuracy Required

As in conventional machine tools, EDM machine tool design and construction is a function of the accuracy required. In cases where positioning accuracy need not be held closer than .001 or .002 in., a conventional coordinate table can be used to obtain position readout from the lead screw via the handwheel dial. In cases where positioning to tenths of thousandths is required, however, a machine should be selected that utilizes an optical readout device, independently of the lead screw.

EDM requires that the axis of the electrode be parallel to the direction of feed for true reproduction of the electrode shape (see Fig. 5-21). Likewise,

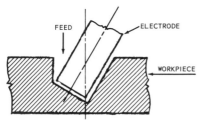

**Fig. 5–21.** Hole deformation due to improper electrode alignment.

where electrodes are mounted on a platen, the platen must be parallel to the top of the table; where electrodes are mounted in a tapered socket, the centerline of the taper must be perpendicular to the table.

### Size of the Workpiece

The larger the workpiece, the more rigid that the machine tool must be to avoid excessive deflection. Although knee type machines are satisfactory for lighter work, bed type machines are required for larger workpieces. In cases where very large workpieces are involved, such as large automotive dies, a four-poster press type of construction (see Fig. 5-22) is recommended.

### Size of the Electrode

The column of the machine tool must be constructed rigidly enough to support the weight of the electrode without excessive deflection. Furthermore, the column must be able to withstand the coolant back pressures peculiar to EDM. Although there is no mechanical interaction between the cutting tool (electrode) and the workpiece as there is in conventional machining, there still can be considerable separating force between the electrode and the workpiece due to coolant pressure. For example, at 25 psi. coolant pressure, a 10 in. square electrode can exert 2500 lbs. of separating force.

**Fig. 5–22.** Four poster machine.
*(Courtesy, Elox Corporation of Michigan)*

**Fig. 5–23.** Two column machine. *(Courtesy, Elox Corporation of Michigan)*

For very large separating forces, it is desirable to keep the throat distance (the distance between the column and the centerline of the spindle) as short as possible to minimize the bending moment about the column. In a single column machine, the column must be quite massive to support the load of the separating force. If a double column machine design (Fig. 5-23) is used, the column can be lighter and still support the load because the work table can be positioned between the columns to reduce the effective throat distance.

### Depth of the Cavity

One of the most important design considerations in an EDM machine tool is the amount of quill travel obtainable under servo feed. Most tool room machines have quill travels in the range from 5 to 12 in. In cases where it is necessary to get down into very deep cavities, and where servo feed is not a requirement through the entire stroke, two types of standard machines are available, having the additional capacity necessary. In a knee type machine, the knee can be positioned so that the electrode is inside the hole yet still at the top of the servo stroke. In a bed-type machine having the head mounted on a secondary slide, the head can be lowered manually on the secondary slide (as on the machine in Fig. 5-16) until the electrode is inside the hole. Movement, in both the knee-type and the head slide type of machine, provides the means of bringing the workpiece and the electrode closer together so that the entire servo stroke can be used for machining. In the fixed ram type of machine, the extra stroke is used for accessibility to the work.

### Orientation of the Cavity

In certain cases, it is necessary to EDM holes, slots, and forms at angles off the vertical plane. This can be accomplished by repositioning the workpiece or by using a knee type machine or a bed type quill machine, both of which permit swiveling of the head to the right or left of vertical.

## Servo Control System

EDM requires that a constant arc gap be maintained between the electrode and the workpiece to obtain maximum machining efficiency. Therefore, every precision EDM tool incorporates some form of servo control to maintain the proper gap spacing. An electro-hydraulic servo control is used in the great majority of EDM machine tools. A typical electro-hydraulic servo system consists of a hydraulic power pack, servo valve and hydraulic cylinder. As cutting proceeds, the servo control system automatically advances the electrode at the rate required to keep the gap constant. If the gap becomes blocked with particles from the cut, the control system automatically retracts the electrode to allow the cutting area to clear, then returns the electrode to the cutting position.

The power supply controls the movement of the head by means of an electro-hydraulic servo valve. By measuring the electrical conditions at the gap and comparing those conditions with a reference in the power supply, a correction signal is generated. The correction signal is transmitted to the servo valve which, in turn, controls the rate and direction of movement of the hydraulic cylinder to reposition the electrode. Thus, the electrode is in almost constant minute movement so as to maintain continuous machining.

The incorporation of servo control systems gives many EDM machines a semi-automatic feature in the form of an adjustable micrometer stop and limit switch mechanism by which the operator can preset the desired depth of cut. When cutting has progressed to the proper depth, the limit switch stops both the head movement and cutting power.

## Dielectric Distribution System

Every EDM machine tool has some form of dielectric distribution system. A typical system consists of a dielectric reservoir, pressure pump, filter, work pan, valves, gages, and plumbing. The dielectric system is basically a recirculating system with the pressure pump forcing the dielectric through the filter to the work and electrode. Dielectric flow pressure is adjustable.

Dielectric typically is stored in the machine base or an auxiliary reservoir. A fast fill pump and motor system or a low pressure air fill system are usually used to transfer the dielectric from the reservoir to the work pan; the dielectric is usually returned to the reservoir through a gravity drain.

Debris produced by the machining operation must be removed from the dielectric, usually by filtration. This process does not affect the dielectric fluid which is continuously reusable.

## ELECTRODE MATERIALS

How well the EDM process performs depends, to a large extent, upon the electrode materials selected, but various electrode materials perform differently when used with different types of power supplies. As pointed out by the discussions under "Power Supply Circuits," many different types of power supplies are in use today. One of the principal objectives in making improvements in these power supplies was to improve the *performance* of the electrode materials used. A further benefit has been to extend the *range* of electrode materials that can be used.

It has been found that the major controlling factors of wear ratios, metal removal rates, and cutting stability are functions of the power supply circuit, rather than functions of the physical or electrical properties of the electrode material. For this reason, it is impossible to provide a fixed set of rules for electrode use.

## Wear Ratios

Electrode wear ratios have been a subject of confusion stemming primarily from the fact that wear ratios and metal removal rates are variables depending upon the type of application, as well as the type of power supplies used. In any one cut, the electrode's end wear ratio and corner wear ratio are different depending upon whether it is a roughing or finishing operation. For example, graphite electrodes have extremely good wear ratios in roughing operations. Furthermore, in roughing applications, sharp-corner definition can be ignored; therefore, the end wear condition is the only critical factor.

Wear ratios are a comparison between the work done and the wear experienced by the electrode. Mathematically, it is written as:

$$\text{Wear Ratio} = \frac{\text{Workpiece Material Removed}}{\text{Loss of Electrode Material}} \qquad (7)$$

In using this mathematical expression, the units of measurement must be common to both the work and the electrode. These units of measurement are normally linear, but some wear ratios are expressed as a comparison between volumes of workpiece metal removed vs. volumes of electrode wear. Fig. 5-24

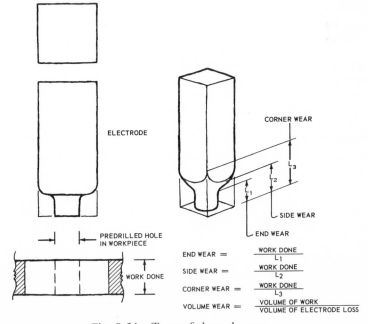

**Fig. 5-24.**   Types of electrode wear.

is a sketch of an EDM through-hole cut in which the various linear measurements that can be made are illustrated. In practical situations, the corner wear ratio is the only useful description of the wear and, as illustrated in Fig. 5-24, it will have the least impressive value.

### Material Selection and Economics

The selection of an electrode material is an economic decision. The cost of the material, itself, is probably the most insignificant factor in the true analysis of the economics involved. The outstanding factors are the ability to produce the electrode to the shape required and the number of cuts that can be made within an acceptable tolerance by that material, i.e., machinability and stability of the material. If the shape required is simple to machine, then the less-expensive electrode materials are more attractive.

However, if a slot must be made in which tolerance control is in the .0005 in. range, then the electrode material must be stable when conventionally machined. For these accuracies, brass and copper are not good materials, since they tend to warp, twist, and produce rough finishes when ground. Better electrode materials for machining to close tolerances are copper-tungsten or silver tungsten, since they are stable under grinding conditions and can be made to have a smooth surface finish.

Table V-5 can be used to assist the EDM user in selecting electrode materials. The table lists the various electrode materials commonly used, the characteristics they exhibit for EDM, and their applications and limitations.

## APPLICATIONS

As mentioned earlier, the EDM process is used to manufacture both tools and parts. The decision to use EDM for either of these broad applications is usually based on one or more of the basic characteristics inherent in the process. Specific applications, such as those described below, have resulted from developments in EDM techniques worked out by many users of the equipment as a means of solving particular problems. EDM equipment has improved substantially in the past few years to make many profitable applications possible.

### Stamping Dies

EDM provides economic advantages for making stamping tools ranging from the most intricate small dies for parts such as gears, up to and including the largest tools used for automobile body parts. The prime advantage of the process is that one portion of the die is made mechanically, and the other half (or more) of the die is matched by EDM at a fraction of the cost and skill required by other means.

The "matching" of dies by means of EDM is a very significant feature that makes the process even more attractive. Also influencing the economic comparison of conventionally-made tools vs. EDM tools is the fact that less sectionalizing in construction is required and, therefore, less fitting is necessary. Since the final matching operations are performed after the steels are hardened, heat-treatment distortion problems are also eliminated, along with the effects of decarburization.

In addition, EDM makes simplified and improved tool designs possible. Perforating punches for multiple piercing of dies can be of one-piece construction and thereby substantially improve the strength of the punch cluster. The design is further simplified by eliminating complex and costly punch-retainer details.

### Extruding Dies

Conventionally machined extruding dies are made by filing a template, laying out the die blank, rough-machining the opening, relieving the back of the die, and finish-filing the die opening prior to the heat-treatment. In addition, the die will normally need to be "touched up" to eliminate the distortion caused by heat-treatment.

Through the proper use of the EDM process, an electrode can be produced in place of the template. The electrode can be used to lay out the die opening and then to finish it after it has been roughed-out (see Fig. 5-25). The EDM operation can take place either before or after heat-treatment, depending upon the size of the die openings and the tolerances required.

**Fig. 5–25.** Extrusion dies and electrodes. (*Courtesy, Elox Corporation of Michigan*)

### Header Dies

Header dies, with irregularly-shaped cavities, are usually manufactured by hobbing which requires that a mild steel be used which is heat-treated and case-hardened after hobbing. The milder steel is less wear-resistant than high-alloy steels, but the high-alloy steels cannot be hobbed. Through the application of EDM, the higher-alloy steels can be used for header dies and their longer tool life results in production runs of from 4 to 7 times that of hobbed steels. Carbide dies can also be made by the same processing techniques with the only increased cost being that of the carbide material. The use of carbide also provides longer tool-life benefits.

Header dies are very simple to produce by EDM. Usually, they are concentric

**Table V-5. Electrode Materials and Their Characteristics**

| Materials | Form | Use With | | Type of Cutting | End Wear for Roughing | Corner Wear for Finishing | Cost | Machinability | Type of Metal Used With | Best Applications | Limitations and Undesirable Uses |
|---|---|---|---|---|---|---|---|---|---|---|---|
| | | RC | Pulse Circuit | | | | | | | | |
| Graphite | blocks, rod, tubes, bars | D | A | roughing finish | 100:1 | 5:1 | A | A | principally steel | all tooling | carbide |
| Copper tungsten | short bars, flats, shim stock, rod, wire, tube | A | A | semi-finish, finishing | 8:1 | 3:1 | B | C | all metals | carbide slots, thin slots | large areas |
| Brass | bar, rod, tube, sheets, wire, rubber stampings | C | A | rough finishes | 1:1 | .7:1 | A | B | all metals | holes | extreme tolerance deep slots |
| Copper | bars, rod, tube, coined plated shapes, forged stampings | A | B | rough finishes | 2:1 | 1:1 | A | B | all metals | holes | extreme tolerance deep slots |
| Silver tungsten | compacted and infiltrated short bars | A | A | semi-finish, finishing | 12:1 | 8:1 | C | C | all metals | small slots and holes | large areas |
| Tungsten | wire, rod, ribbon | B | B | semi-finish, finishing | 10:1 | 5:1 | B | D | all metals, principally refractory | small slots and holes | irregular holes |

| Material | Form | | | | | | | | all metals, principally refractory | small slots and holes | irregular holes |
|---|---|---|---|---|---|---|---|---|---|---|---|
| Tungsten carbide | sintered rod | B | B | semi-finish, finishing | 10:1 | 6:1 | A | A | non-ferrous | through-holes | carbide |
| Steel | All | D | C | semi-finish | 4:1 | 1:1 | | | steels | stamping dies | |
| Zinc | cast shapes | D | C | rough, semi-finish | 1.5:1 | 7:1 | A | B | steels only | forging die cavities only | holes |
| Zamac | cast shapes | D | C | rough, semi-finish | 2:1 | .5:1 | A | B | steels only | forging die cavities only | — |
| Aluminum | cast shaped, forged | D | C | rough, medium | 2:1 | .5:1 | A | B | steels only | forging die cavities only | — |
| Hafnium | wire, ribbon | B | A | semi-finish, finishing | 15:1 | 10:1 | D | — | refractory | thin slots, small holes only | — |
| Molybdenum | rod, wire, tube | A | B | medium finish | 8:1 | 3:1 | C | — | refractory | holes only | — |
| Nickel | plated shapes | A | A | medium finish | 8:1 | 5:1 | C | C | all metals | intricate cavity detail only | — |

Legend:  A = Excellent
B = Good
C = Fair
D = Poor

in form; therefore, fixturing requirements are little more than simple pot-chucks. The electrodes used are straight lengths of the form required as shown in Fig. 5-26. EDM processing consists of a series of identical passes to the full depth of the cavity required. After each pass, the worn portion of the electrode is removed in order to achieve sharpness in the. bottom of the header cavity.

**Fig. 5–26.**  Header dies and electrodes. *(Courtesy, Elox Corporation of Michigan)*

**Fig. 5–27.**  Wire drawing dies. *(Courtesy, Elox Corporation of Michigan)*

Hammers for header dies having shapes that are difficult to produce conventionally, can be produced simply by EDM on any high-alloy steel. In particular, those hammers that require raised letters for designs can be produced by engraving the electrode and using it to cut away the unwanted steel, leaving the raised design that is desired.

In addition to the advantage of longer production runs from the higher-alloy steels, the cost of dies produced by EDM is also reduced through the salvage of worn dies. Since it is not necessary to anneal the worn die, it can be reprocessed to the next larger size with the proper electrodes. The salvage operation takes less time than the production of a new tool and, in addition, saves all the preparatory operations of the die-nib.

### Wire-Drawing Dies

Although wire-drawing dies are relatively simple in configuration, the materials used (such as carbide) make them extremely difficult to produce by conventional methods. Such difficult conventional operations as grinding and honing are replaced by turning of the electrodes, followed by the EDM operation and a slight polishing of the die opening (see Fig. 5-27).

Wire-drawing dies, like header dies, can also be salvaged through EDM by making the die openings to the next larger size. This represents a considerable economic saving because of the great number of die sizes required in the wire-producing industry.

### Molds

Molding cavities, because of their intricate shapes, require many mechanical cutting and benching operations. Costly inserting is used in conventional mold building, which adds hours to the design and building of the tools. While these added hours represent a distinct disadvantage, a less desirable tool also results. Inserts, no matter how closely fitted, become evident in service by leaving witness marks on the molded product. One of the main advantages of EDM in mold building is its ability to produce the intricate shapes required without inserting (see Fig. 5-28) and, in addition, provide a longer-lasting, better tool.

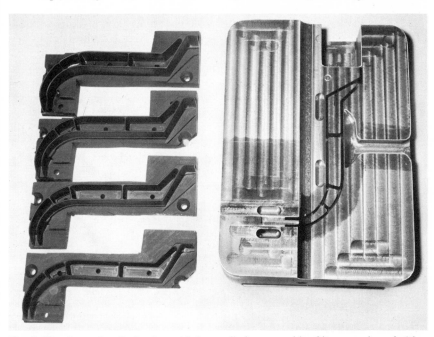

**Fig. 5–28.** Irregular rib slots in mold electro-discharge machined in approximately 3 hrs. *(Courtesy, The Ingersoll Milling Machine Company)*

Raised lettering and designs in molds are extremely costly to produce conventionally, but represent outstanding EDM applications. Removing the background area around raised letters conventionally requires a great deal of the engraver's time; therefore, the cost of such engraving is quite high. By performing this operation with EDM, the advantages are two-fold: (1) engraving of the electrode only requires the machining of the letter or design shape, and (2) electrode materials are easily machined.

When using EDM for engraving, the workpiece can be in the hardened state, eliminating any possibility of distortion or decarburization due to heat-treatment. In addition to being a superior method of engraving raised configurations, EDM makes it possible to engrave work in deep, out-of-reach areas with considerable ease.

When mold halves have an irregular mating surface (referred to as a parting line) it is extremely difficult and time-consuming to conventionally seat the surfaces satisfactorily. Machining the surfaces reasonably closely is not the problem; the problem lies in the highly-skilled operations required to fit the two surfaces closely enough to prevent leakage during the molding operation. EDM is being used extensively in matching the parting lines of molds. In this application, cutting occurs between the 2 closest points of the mold halves and is continued until the entire contact face area has been electrically matched. Mold matching by EDM is usually done in approximately $^1/_8$ of the time required by conventional methods.

### Forging Dies

The primary application of EDM in making forging dies, is the production of the entire cavity form. To make forging tools,·the die cavities are usually roughed-out by conventional machining or by a high metal-removal-rate EDM power supply. The final sizing of the cavity is done with fully-contoured electrodes, usually made by duplicating graphite blocks on a 3-dimensional duplicator. Until recently, the predominant method of producing full-form cavity electrodes was by casting a zinc-tin mixture in an existing steel master tool.

Most forging dies are sunk originally and then resunk 2 or more times as the cavity wears. For this reason, the resinking operations already have a "roughed-out" condition since the top face of the tools are machined away leaving a partial cavity for the EDM operation to complete.

The production of forging dies by EDM has advanced substantially due to the advent of good graphite electrode materials, practical methods of producing full-contoured electrodes, and improvements in EDM equipment. An example is shown in Fig. 5-29.

**Fig. 5–29.** Forging die for jet engine impeller 12 in. in diameter, sunk by EDM from a solid block in approximately 24 hrs. A total of 88 cu. in. of metal was removed. *(Courtesy, The Ingersoll Milling Machine Company)*

### Production Work

The economic justification for using EDM on production work is based upon capitalizing on the basic phenomena of the process. Exotic metals, used extensively today in the aerospace industries, can be machined by EDM just as easily as the mild steels. Conventional machining of refractory metals, carbides, hardened steels, and work-hardening steels all present problems that invite the investigation of EDM.

Unusual or difficult geometries, such as acute-angle entrance of holes, often dictate the use of EDM since there is no contact force that would tend to force the cutting tool away from the workpiece and prevent accurate acute-angle hole-drilling. An example of such a production part is shown in Fig. 5-30 which is a jet engine vane. A special production machine was used to drill 13, .050 in. diameter holes in 4 of these parts simultaneously. Electrodes and workpieces were set up on a shuttle arrangement; while the machine is cutting one side, the operator can unload and reload the opposite side. The electrodes used were inexpensive centerless ground brass rods.

The use of EDM is attractive even for "easy-to-machine" metals where a burr would be produced by conventional methods. Often, the combined cost of conventional machining and deburring compares favorably with EDM on an economic basis.

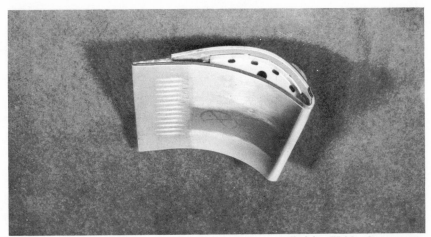

**Fig. 5–30.** Holes in trailing edge of jet engine vane drilled by EDM. *(Courtesy, Elox Corporation of Michigan)*

Delicate workpieces that are not strong enough to support the cutting load of conventional tools can be processed by EDM without distortion. For instance, the electronics industry uses many EDM machines in the production of small, thin copper vacuum tube parts.

Sometimes accuracy requirements dictate the use of EDM for two main reasons: (1) when repetitive shapes are required, they can often be produced from an easy-to-make male electrode, and (2) when machining accuracy must be maintained after heat-treatment of the part.

The various discussions of EDM applications above are by no means complete nor could they be, because the successful use of EDM is the result of using this metal removal method to solve particular manufacturing problems.

## RECENT DEVELOPMENTS

The EDM process has been under development for many years. The most recent development has been an improvement in the wear effect of graphite electrodes cutting steel when used with rotary impulse generator power supplies, transistorized power supplies and, most recently, tube-type power supplies. In some of the transistorized power supplies, the wear characteristics of copper electrodes cutting steel have also been improved.

In most tube-type power supplies, the improvement in wear is achieved at a sacrifice in metal removal rate. The use of the low-wear techniques should be based on a thorough cost analysis that takes into account both the machining time as well as the cost of the electrodes.

The cost of production EDM systems represents approximately $1/5$ of the cost of conventional equipment capable of the same production. The user also has the advantage of less floor space and substantially reduced manpower requirements.

#### REFERENCE

1. P. E. Berghausen, *et al.*, "Electro-Discharge Machining Program," *Final Report, ASD-TDR-7-545* (July, 1963). Available from Defense Document Center, Arlington Hall Station, Arlington, Virginia (DDC Final No. AD423-199).

# THERMO-ELECTRIC PROCESSES

The thermo-electric processes discussed in this chapter are: electron beam machining (EBM), laser machining (LBM), plasma arc machining (PAM), and ion beam machining (IBM). These are categorized as thermo-electric processes because each utilizes thermal energy to remove material, and each uses electrical energy, in some way, to generate the thermal energy. In EBM, a stream of high-speed electrons impinges on the workpiece where its kinetic energy is transformed into thermal energy. In LBM, the use of electrical energy is less direct, in that it is used as one step in the process of generating, or "stimulating" the emission of the light energy which is then converted to thermal energy on striking the workpiece. In PAM and IBM, an ionized (or electrically-charged) beam or plasma is generated, which is the source of thermal energy for material removal.

The principal unique characteristics of these processes as a group, and those which place them among the more exotic of the non-traditional machining processes, are the high temperatures and high thermal energy densities which can be achieved for material removal (e.g., energy densities of $10^{10}$ w/in² are now being used in EBM and LBM). The concomitant extremely high energy transfer rates and thermal gradients produce processing conditions which have effects on materials that are only beginning to be understood.

At present, although there are instances of competition among some of these processes themselves, the thermo-electric processes are generally used when no other process can do the job. Considerable research and development efforts are being devoted to improving the understanding of the processes, and to achieving the broader application and general acceptance which these processes seem to deserve.

## ELECTRON BEAM MACHINING

Electron beams are used in many types of industrial equipment today. In most cases, this is predicated on the fact that electrons can be accelerated and formed into a narrow beam by an electric field. The beam thus formed can be focused and bent by electrostatic and electromagnetic fields, much as light rays can be focused and bent by glass lenses.

In electron beam cutting and welding machines, relatively high-power beams are used with electron velocities exceeding $\frac{1}{2}$ the speed of light. This high-speed stream of electrons is focused on a very small spot where it impinges upon the material to be treated. At this point, the kinetic energy of the electrons

135

is transformed into thermal energy, vaporizing or melting the material very locally, depending on whether cutting or welding is desired. The process is usually carried out in a vacuum environment to prevent collisions of electrons with gas molecules which would scatter or diffuse the electron beam.

### Process Principles

The principle of electron beam machining (EBM) is based on an extremely high-power-density kinetic energy created by a stream of focused high-velocity electrons which bombard and locally vaporize the workpiece material. A typical EBM system is schematically illustrated in Fig. 6-1.

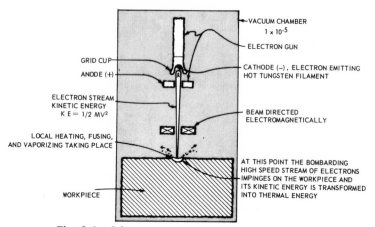

**Fig. 6-1.** Schematic of electron beam machining (EBM).

**Generation of Electron Beam.** The electron beam is formed inside an electron gun which is basically a triode and consists of: (1) a cathode which is a hot tungsten filament emitting high negative potential electrons, (2) a grid cup, negatively biased with respect to the filament, and (3) an anode at ground potential through which the accelerated electrons pass. A stream of electrons is emitted from the tip of the hot cathode and accelerated toward the anode by a high accelerating potential between the anode and the cathode. The degree of negative bias applied to the grid cup controls the flow of electrons, or beam current, and can be used to turn the beam on and off. Due to the shape of the electrostatic field formed by the grid cup, the electrons are simultaneously electrostatically prefocused and pass, as a converging beam, through the hole in the anode without colliding with the anode itself. As soon as the electrons have passed through the anode, they have reached their maximum velocity for a given accelerating voltage, and will maintain this velocity (since the process takes place in a collision-free environment) until they collide with a body which, in this case, is the workpiece.

Generation and transmission of the electron beam takes place in a collision-free environment provided by a vacuum of $10^{-4}$ mm. Hg or better. Such a vacuum can easily be obtained with standard commercial vacuum equipment. Since the impingement of high-velocity electrons results in x-ray emission, it is necessary to shield the chamber with suitable materials to absorb this radiation.

Shielding techniques used are equivalent to those used with commercial x-ray equipment. Appropriate work-handling mechanisms are installed within the vacuum chamber.

*Electron Gun.* The basic equations describing the electron gun are presented in Table VI-1. As illustrated by the sample calculation, with an accelerating potential of 150,000 v., the electrons attain a velocity of 142,000 mi/sec. A "stigmator" magnetic coil, located just below the electron gun, is used to remove astigmatism and give the electron beam a circular cross-section.

*Electron Beam Control.* The electron beam is controlled with optical precision and is a heat source which, with its energy density, precision, and mobility, exceeds any known commercial heat source. Light rays (such as those emitted by a laser), produce electromagnetic wave radiation whose energy content depends on the temperature of the light source. Light rays *cannot be accelerated* to increase the energy content.

Electron emission, on the other hand, differs in principle. The beam consists of negatively charged particles whose energy content is determined by the mass and velocity of the individual particles. And, the negatively charged particles *can be accelerated* in an electrostatic field to extremely high velocities. During this process, the specific energy content of the electron beam can be increased beyond the emission energy, thus producing a beam of energy, the intensity of which far exceeds that obtainable from light. Due to the precise electron optics, large amounts of energy can be manipulated with optical precision.

The electron optical column has a built-in stereo-microscope device which enables the operator to accurately locate the beam impact point and observe the drilling, cutting, or milling operation taking place. This microscope has a hole through the reflecting mirror and objective lens, through which the electron beam passes towards the workpiece. Through the use of visual optics, the operator can view the workpiece coaxially at up to 40 times magnification.

*Refocusing the Beam.* Before the electrons collide with the workpiece, a variable strength electromagnetic lens is used to refocus the beam to any desired diameter down to less than .001 in. at a precise location on the workpiece, and thus attains an extremely high power density. An electron beam having a cross-sectional diameter of .0005 to .001 in. will result in a power density of 10 billion w/sq in. This extremely high-power density immediately vaporizes any material on which the beam impinges (see Fig. 6-1). Thus, in reality, electron beam cutting is a very precisely controlled vaporization process. The basic equations used to determine the energy requirements necessary to vaporize various materials are given in Table VI-1B.

A magnetic deflection coil, mounted below the magnetic lens, is used to bend the beam and direct it over the desired surface of the workpiece. This deflection system permits programming of the beam in any specific geometrical pattern, using the proper deflection coil current input. At the point of beam impingement, the kinetic energy in the beam is converted to thermal energy in the workpiece.

In addition to specific deflection techniques described later under "Applications," another interesting deflection control technique is the "flying spot scanner" or optical tracing device shown schematically in Fig. 6-2. Using this device, the electron beam can be deflected to cover almost any conceivable

## Table VI-1. Basic Equations of EBM

### A. Energy of Electrons

(1) Kinetic energy per electron (K.E.) $= \frac{1}{2}\, mV^2 = Ee$

Where: $mg$ = Weight of electron = $9.1066 \times 10^{-26}$ g
$e$ = Charge on electron = $1.60 \times 10^{-19}$ joules
$E$ = Voltage
$V$ = Velocity of electron (cm/sec)
1 g-cm $= 9.807 \times 10^{-5}$ joules

(2) Number of electrons per sec (N) $= In$

Where: $I$ = Beam current (amps)
$n = 6.3 \times 10^{18}\ \dfrac{\text{electron}}{\text{sec.}}\Big/ \text{amp.}$

(3) Power total $P = EI = EenI$ (watts)
$e \cdot n = 1.0$    1 watt = 1 joule/sec

Sample velocity calculation

$I = 2.5 \times 10^{-5}$ amp, $E = 1.5 \times 10^5$ volts.

$$V^2 = \frac{9.1066 \times 10^{-2}\ \text{g}}{(2)(9.806 \times 10^2\ \text{cm/sec}^2)} \quad \frac{2.4 \times 10^{-14}\ \text{joules}}{9.807 \times 10^{-5}\ \text{joules/g-cm}}$$

$V = 2.3 \times 10^{10}$ cm/sec = 142,000 miles/sec

### B. Energy Required to Vaporize Workpiece

(1) Metal removal rate (G cm³/sec) $= \eta P/W$

Where: $P$ = Power (watts or joules/sec)
$W$ = Specific energy required to vaporize metal (joule/cm³)
$\eta$ = Efficiency (cutting)
$W = [C(T_M - 20°\text{C}) + C(T_B - T_M) + H_f + V_V]$

Where: $C$ = Specific heat
$T_M$ = Melting temperature °C.
$T_B$ = Boiling temperature °C.
$H_f$ = Heat of fusion
$H_V$ = Heat of vaporization

pattern over a $^1/_4$ sq. in. area. The desired pattern is drawn, then photographed, and the photographic negative acts as the master. The areas to be cut appear as transparent lines on the negative; the remainder of the negative is opaque.

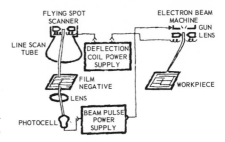

**Fig. 6–2.** Flying spot scanner for electron beam cutting of complex patterns.

Light emitted from a cathode ray tube passes through the transparent lines on the negative and is picked up by a phototube, which relays the signal to a logic system that triggers the electron beam. The deflection coils of the cathode ray tube are coupled directly to coils that deflect the electron beam to the correct position on the workpiece. Any pattern that appears on the negative can be automatically reproduced on the workpiece at 10:1 reduction. Applications include drilling precision grids, etching copper gravure plates, and fabricating precision film resistors.

The electron beam can also be deflected in a predetermined pattern by a relay tray or a flying spot scanner mounted in a control cabinet which consists of a saw-tooth square wave and sine wave generator. For example, if a cross-shaped hole with slots having parallel walls is being cut, a square wave generator and its amplitude would be used to control the length. The cross-shaped hole is cut by using a 4-pole deflection system whereby one set of coils, mounted opposite from each other, is connected to the square wave generator and one pair of coils, mounted 90 deg. to the first set, is connected to the saw-tooth generator. The beam evaporates a thin layer of material, then is switched off by a signal from the relay tray. The deflection coils are then shifted 90 deg. in relation to their initial connection by the relay tray, and the process is repeated. A thin layer of material is thus continuously evaporated from one end of the slot to the other. The beam is switched off, the system is rotated 90 deg. from the previous position, and the other slot is machined. The system is continuously rotated in circles to allow uniform impingement on the material and to correct previous deflection pattern error.

By using this process, it is possible to drill a cross-shaped hole, for example, through a piece of stainless steel .040 in. thick, barely raising the temperature of the surrounding material itself. Extremely high energy density makes it possible to drill the hole while, a few thousandths of an inch away from the wall of the hole, the workpiece remains at room temperature. In operation, the electron optical column is mounted on top of the vacuum chamber and the workpiece is placed inside the vacuum chamber which is evacuated to a pressure of 1.0 times $10^{-5}$. The vacuum chamber prevents the workpiece from becoming contaminated by any foreign material. The heat input into the material is so localized and so extremely high that it is possible to electron beam drill or mill a cross-shaped hole into the head of a pin without melting the pin.

**Cutting Efficiency.** EBM is especially adaptable to cutting very small holes or very narrow slots in thin-gage materials. As illustrated in Fig. 6-3, the cutting efficiency for EBM slotting rises slightly, peaks out, and then drops rapidly as

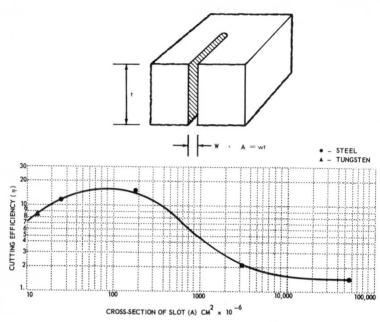

**Fig. 6–3.** Efficiency of EBM slotting.

the slot cross-sectional area increases. To minimize heating and melting adjacent to the cut, extremely short beam "on" pulses of several microseconds are used with considerably longer beam "off" periods between pulses to permit dissipation, by thermal conductivity, of any incidental heating adjacent to the cut. The cutting efficiency is, therefore, much lower than the actual efficiency of the equipment, since the power is "off" a large percentage of the time.

Assuming a cutting efficiency of 15 per cent (Fig. 6-3) and using the physical properties given in Table VI-2, the metal removal rates vs. power can be

## Table VI-2. Physical Thermal Properties of Various Metals

| Property \ Material | Aluminum | Titanium | Molybdenum | Tungsten | Iron |
|---|---|---|---|---|---|
| Melting temperature °C. | 660 | 1668 | 2610 | 3410 | 1536 |
| Boiling temperature °C. | 2450 | 3260 | 5560 | 5930 | 3000 |
| Specific heat cal/g/°C. (C) | .215 | .126 | .061 | .032 | .11 |
| Heat of fusion cal/g ($H_f$) | 94.6 | 36.7 | 70.0 | 44.0 | 65 |
| Heat of vaporization cal/g ($H_v$) | 2517.6 | 2223.4 | 1340 | 1005.9 | 1514.8 |
| Specific energy to vaporize (W) $\dfrac{\text{joules}}{\text{cm}^3}$ | $3.54 \times 10^4$ | $5.07 \times 10^4$ | $7.46 \times 10^4$ | $1.0 \times 10^5$ | $6.28 \times 10^4$ |

determined from the equation in Table VI-1*B*. This is shown graphically in Fig. 6-4. The data in Fig. 6-4 are based on a pulse width of 80 sec. and a pulse frequency of 50 cps. For every second of actual cutting time, the machine is "off" .996 sec.

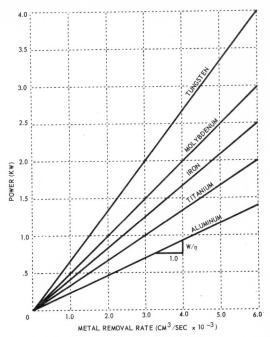

**Fig. 6–4.** Metal removal rates vs. power (assuming 15 per cent cutting efficiency).

### Advantages and Limitations

Only relatively small cuts are economically feasible with EBM techniques since the material removal rate is approximately 0.1 mg/sec. However, EBM makes possible the production of very precise and fine cuts of any desired contour in any material. In addition, there is no tool pressure or tool wear, and the process is very adaptable to automatic programming. The following representative applications illustrate the capabilities of electron beam cutting. A summary of the advantages and limitations of EBM are listed in Table VI-3.

### Applications

Typical applications for EBM are:

1) Drilling gas orifices for pressure differential devices, whereby closely dimensioned holes are drilled through the part. These holes regulate the amount of gas that flows in a given amount of time. Such devices are used in space nuclear reactors, rotor and stator blades for supersonic aircraft engines, etc.

2) Producing wire-drawing dies, light ray orifices, and spinnerets to produce synthetic fibers.

## Table VI-3. Advantages and Limitations of EBM

| Advantages | Limitations |
|---|---|
| 1) Most precise cutting tool available. | 1) All cutting must be done in a vacuum. Vacuum chamber requires batch processing. Size of vacuum tends to restrict size of part. Time required to evacuate chamber. |
| 2) Can cut holes of very small size (down to .002 in. diameter). | 2) Only relatively small cuts are economically feasible since the material removal rate is approximately .1 mg/sec or approximately .0001 in³/min. |
| 3) Can cut any known material, metal or non-metal, that will exist in high vacuum. | 3) Holes produced have a slight crater where beam enters work and also has small taper (4-degree included angle). Hole geometry in depth direction varies with material thickness because the beam fans out above and below its focal point. This beam divergence tends to produce an hourglass shape, especially in small deep holes. |
| 4) Excellent for micromachining. | |
| 5) No cutting tool pressure or wear. | |
| 6) Cuts holes with high depth to diameter ratios (200:1 ratio). | |
| 7) .001 in. wide slots can be machined. | |
| 8) Because of small beam diameter (.005 in.) extremely close tolerances can be held (±.00005 to .0002 in.). Positioning can be held to ±.0005 or better with handling devices. | 4) Equipment cost is high. |
| 9) Very adaptable to automatic machining. | 5) Requires high operator skill. |
| 10) Can drill holes and end mill slots or orifices that cannot be machined by any other process. | 6) Usually only applicable to thin parts, .010 to .250 in. range. |
| 11) Distortion free machining of thin foils and hollow wall parts. | |
| 12) Precise control of energy input over wide range. | |
| 13) Extremely fast cutting speeds per hole, averaging 1 sec/hole. Cutting speeds, depending on material composition and thickness, range from less than 2 to more than 24 in/min. Largest part of cycle time is setup and chamber pump down-time. | |
| 14) No physical or metallurgical damage results. Heat affected zone is practically non-existent. | |

3) Producing metering holes, either round or profile shaped, to be used as flow holes on sleeve valves, rocket fuel injectors, or injection nozzles on diesel engines.

The electron beam milling or drilling processes by no means compete with EDM or ECM machines, or vice versa, due to the fact that the applicability of electron beam drilling stops where the applicability of EDM or ECM equipment starts.

**Hole Drilling.** In drilling holes, the electron beam focuses on one spot and evaporates material until it has completely penetrated the workpiece, or until it is switched off after a specified hole depth has been reached. Hole diameter depends on beam diameter and energy density. If holes larger than the beam diameter are required, then the electron beam is deflected electromagnetically in a circular path as described above. The diameter of the hole can be changed by varying the amplitude of the voltage generator connected to the electromagnetic deflection system. If extremely large holes are required, the workpiece can be moved off-center and rotated.

Typical data on drilling holes by EBM are given in Table VI-4 which shows, once again, that materials ranging from very soft to hard and brittle can be

**Table VI-4. Holes Drilled by EBM in Various Materials**

| Material | Thickness (in.) | Hole Diameter (in.) | Drilling Speed (sec.) | Accelerating Voltage (kv.) | Average Beam Current (micro-amps) | Pulse Width (micro-sec.) | Pulse Frequency (cps.) |
|---|---|---|---|---|---|---|---|
| 400 Series stainless steel | .010 | .0005 | <1 | 130 | 60 | 4 | 3000 |
| Alumina Al₂O₃ | .030 | .012 | 30 | 125 | 60 | 80 | 50 |
| Tungsten | .010 | .001 | <1 | 140 | 50 | 20 | 50 |
| 90-10 tantalum-tungsten | .040 | .005 | <1 | 140 | 100 | 80 | 50 |
| 90-10 tantalum-tungsten | .080 | .005 | 10 | 140 | 100 | 80 | 50 |
| 90-10 tantalum-tungsten | .100 | .005 | 10 | 140 | 100 | 80 | 50 |
| Stainless steel | .040 | .005 | <1 | 140 | 100 | 80 | 50 |
| Stainless steel | .080 | .005 | 10 | 140 | 100 | 80 | 50 |
| Stainless steel | .100 | .005 | 10 | 140 | 100 | 80 | 50 |
| Aluminum | .100 | .005 | 10 | 140 | 100 | 80 | 50 |
| Tungsten | .016 | .003 | <1 | 130 | 100 | 80 | 50 |
| Quartz | .125 | .001 | <1 | 140 | 10 | 12 | 50 |

successfully drilled and that, although the holes are very fine, drilling time is extremely short. In general, holes less than .005 in. in diameter can be drilled almost instantaneously in thicknesses up to .050 in. in any material. Hole diameters larger than .005 in. can be drilled by deflecting or rotating the electron beam. The smallest hole that has been drilled to date measured .0025 in. in diameter and was cut in .004 in. thick brass shim stock.

Most EBM drilled holes are characterized by a small crater on the beam incident side of the workpiece and are usually slightly tapered, with the minimum diameter occurring at the beam exit side of the workpiece. It has been observed that holes drilled in material less than .005 in. thick exhibit little or no wall taper while, in heavier sections, a taper of 2 to 4 deg. included angle usually is encountered. Examples of EBM drilling are shown in Figs. 6-5 through 6-8.

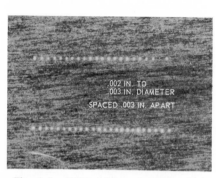

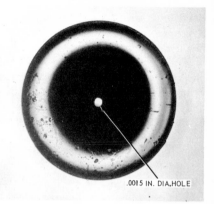

**Fig. 6–5.** EBM drilling of .010 in. thick molybdenum. *(Courtesy, Hamilton Standard, Division of United Aircraft Corporation)*

**Fig. 6–6.** Synthetic sapphire jewel bearing (1.0 sec. cutting time). *(Courtesy, Hamilton Standard, Division of United Aircraft Corporation)*

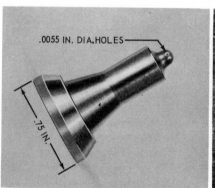

**Fig. 6–7.** Stainless steel injection nozzle. *(Courtesy, Hamilton Standard, Division of United Aircraft Corporation)*

**Fig. 6–8.** .042 sq. in. holes drilled in .010 in. thick molybdenum. *(Courtesy, Hamilton Standard, Division of United Aircraft Corporation)*

**Cutting Slots.** Table VI-5 shows the rate at which slots have been cut in a variety of materials by EBM. Cutting speeds, in general, are dependent upon the amount of material to be removed, i.e., the cross-section of the slot to be cut. This is illustrated by the curve in Fig. 6-3 and the data in Table VI-5.

All EBM cut slots exhibit a small amount of material splatter on the beam incident side, which can usually be removed by a light abrasive cleaning. EBM slots in materials less than .005 in. thick have extremely parallel sides with essentially no wall taper. The width of the slot measured at the top and bottom can usually be maintained at ±.001 in. tolerance. The walls of EBM slots in

**Table VI-5. Slots Cut by EBM in Various Materials**

| Material | Thickness (in.) | Slot Description and/or Dimensions (in.) | Cutting Speed | Accelerating Voltage (kv.) | Average Beam (micro-amps) | Pulse Width (micro-sec.) | Pulse Frequency (cps.) |
|---|---|---|---|---|---|---|---|
| Stainless steel | .062 | Rectangle: .008 by .250 | 5 min. | 140 | 120 | 80 | 50 |
| Hardened steel | .125 | Rectangle: .018 by .072 | 10 min. | 140 | 150 | 80 | 50 |
| Stainless steel | .007 | .004 wide | 2 in/min | 130 | 50 | 80 | 50 |
| Brass | .010 | .004 wide | 2 in/min | 130 | 50 | 80 | 50 |
| Stainless steel | .002 | .002 wide | 4 in/min | 130 | 20 | 4 | 50 |
| Alumina Al$_2$O$_3$ | .030 | .004 wide | 24 in/min | 150 | 200 | 80 | 200 |
| Tungsten | .002 | .001 wide | 7 in/min | 150 | 30 | 80 | 50 |

materials .005 to .125 in. thick exhibit a taper of 1 to 2 deg. The edges of the walls can be maintained parallel to a tolerance of .002 in. The narrowest slots cut to date by EBM have been in materials approximately .001 in. thick and have had a width slightly less than .001 in. When cutting slots of these dimensions, it is often necessary to make more than one pass in order to obtain a sharp, smooth edge. Examples of slots cut by EBM are shown in Figs. 6-9 through 6-11.

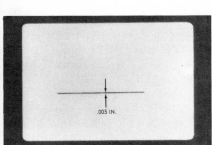

**Fig. 6–9.** Slot cut at 24 in/min in .030 in. aluminum oxide wafer. (*Courtesy, Hamilton Standard, Division of United Aircraft Corporation*)

**Fig. 6–10.** Dicing of silicon chips for semiconductor industry. (*Courtesy, Hamilton Standard, Division of United Aircraft Corporation*)

**Milling.** In drilling or milling production quantities with EBM, automatic and sometimes tape-controlled tooling is used to index and position the work-

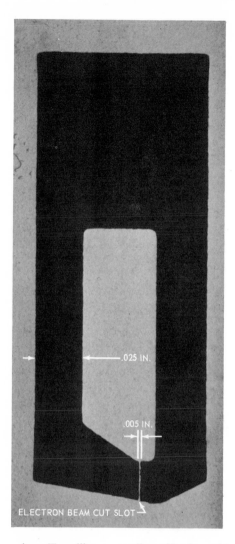

**Fig. 6-11.** Ferrite memory core (.005 in. thick). *(Courtesy, Hamilton Standard, Division of United Aircraft Corporation)*

piece. To mill very small profile-shaped holes (less than $^1/_4$ in. sq.), the workpiece remains stationary while the electron beam is programmed to cut the pattern. This is done by sending electrical signals from the programming circuits to the electromagnetic deflection system which, in turn, generates a magnetic field which moves the electron beam in a predetermined pattern. The beam remains essentially stationary at one point for the duration of a pulse. As each succeeding pulse occurs, the beam is repositioned by the deflection system. This process repeats automatically many times per minute and the beam scans over the same pattern until the hole is completed and the beam has been switched off.

### Future Potential

EBM techniques offer a new and valuable approach to industry for the precise removal of small amounts of material. The practical examples described above are only a few of the many applications that can be successfully accomplished by the EBM process. Undoubtedly, as the unusual capabilities of EBM become more generally known and more fully understood, these processes will play an ever-increasing role in industrial metalworking operations.

## LASER BEAM MACHINING

"Laser" is an acronym for *L*ight *A*mplification by *S*timulated *E*mission of *R*adiation. Although the laser is used as a light amplifier in some applications, its chief use is as an optical oscillator or transducer for converting energy into a highly collimated beam of optical radiation (light). The light energy emitted by the laser has several characteristics which distinguish it from other light sources:

1) Spectral Purity — The light emitted by the laser is very monochromatic and permits the use of simple lenses for focusing the beam (i.e., color-corrected lenses are not required).
2) Directivity — The light beam emitted by the laser is highly collimated with typical divergence angles of $10^{-2}$ to $10^{-4}$ radians.
3) High Focused Power Density — As a result of its small beam divergence, all of the laser beam energy can be collected with simple optics and focused onto a small area. A beam of light which diverges by a small angle $\theta$ (Fig. 6-12) can be focused with a lens to a spot having a diameter given by:

$$S = f\theta \qquad (1)$$

where $S$ is the spot diameter, $f$ is the focal length of the lens, and $\theta$ is the beam divergence in radians. The small beam divergence of lasers is responsible for achieving high power densities in local areas which are reasonably distant from the focusing optics.

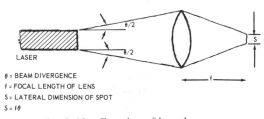

θ = BEAM DIVERGENCE
f = FOCAL LENGTH OF LENS
S = LATERAL DIMENSION OF SPOT
S = fθ

**Fig. 6–12.**   Focusing of laser beam.

## Process Principles

Before discussing types of laser systems and their applications to machining, a brief explanation of the fundamental principles involved will aid understanding. As in many of the advanced processes, the fundamental principle of a laser must be explained on an atomic level.

An atom's orbital electrons can jump to higher energy levels (orbits further away from the nucleus) by absorbing quanta of stimulating energy. When this occurs, the atom is said to be in the "excited" state and may then spontaneously emit, or radiate, the absorbed energy. Simultaneously, the electron drops back to its original orbit (ground state) or to an intermediate level. If, while the atom is in the excited state, another quantum of energy is absorbed by the electron, 2 quanta of energy are radiated, and the electron drops to the lower energy level. The stimulated or radiated energy has precisely the same wavelength as that of the stimulating energy. As a result, the stimulating energy (pumping radiation) is amplified as shown in Fig. 6-13. This principle is the basis of laser operation.

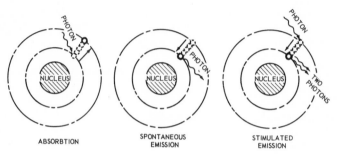

**Fig. 6-13.**  Laser principle.

In order for the laser to capture stimulating energy in the form of coherent light, i.e., all the light waves are in step, and intensify it to a high power density, certain basic components are necessary as illustrated in Fig. 6-14. In Fig. 6-14, the light radiated by the excited electrons is in phase with the beam which

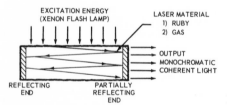

**Fig. 6-14.**  Basic laser components.

initiated the reaction. As the now-intensified light continues to travel back and forth through the laser material, more and more electrons are stimulated into giving up their energy, all in phase with the constantly building signal. As the light is reflected and surges back and forth in the tube, it soon becomes so powerful that a ray bursts forth from the partially reflecting end.

### Types of Lasers

Many types of lasers exist which produce highly directive beams of optical or infrared radiation. Only a few of these, however, are both powerful and reliable enough to be useful for practical machining operations. The two types of laser systems which show the greatest potential are: the pulsed optically pumped solid state laser, and the continuous $CO_2$-$N_2$ molecular laser.

**$CO_2$-$N_2$ Gas Laser.**  This is a relatively new device which shows great promise of becoming an effective machine tool. The $CO_2$-$N_2$ laser generally uses 3 gases flowing through a glass discharge tube (the gas has recently been added to the $CO_2$ to improve efficiency). An electrical discharge is then generated through the gases, and the $N_2$ and the molecules transfer energy to the $CO_2$ molecules which can then generate a continuous beam of infrared radiation at 10.6 microns. Since most types of glass are highly absorbent at 10.6 microns, mirrors replace the lenses for focusing the output beam.

This laser, even though it is a relatively new device, has two outstanding features. First, the $CO_2$-$N_2$ laser is capable of relatively high, continuous power outputs (approximately 1.0 kw at this time) and second, it has already been demonstrated to have a conversion efficiency greater than 13 per cent (high for laser devices). This efficiency is not yet near the theoretical limit but experts in the field expect efficiencies greater than 20 per cent in the near future. The $CO_2$-$N_2$ laser has the characteristic low beam divergence of lasers and can easily be focused onto spot diameters of a few thousandths of an inch. If an output power of only 100 w. focused onto a spot .004 in. in diameter is assumed, the resulting power density will be approximately 80 Mw/sq in. While this device could be expected to replace the electron beam machine for many applications not requiring a vacuum surrounding the workpiece, both for reasons of cost and convenience, the $CO_2$-$N_2$ laser must still be considered a laboratory device. However, several manufacturers are beginning to market low power systems (15 to 25 w. of output) and larger systems can be expected on the market soon.

**Optically Pumped Solid State Laser.** This laser produces the highest energy and peak power output of any existing pulsed laser. It is this characteristic, together with its low beam divergence and high reliability which makes the optically pumped solid state laser very attractive for industrial machining applications. Ruby and neodymium-in-glass are the two optically pumped solid state laser materials that appear best for industrial application because of their laser characteristics and also their superior physical properties.

The ruby laser material is crystalline aluminum oxide (sapphire) which contains about a fraction of 1.0 per cent concentration of chromium ions distributed throughout the aluminum lattice sites. The neodymium-in-glass laser material uses various kinds of glass as the host material with a concentration of 2 to 6 per cent by weight of neodymium (Nd). Both the ruby and Nd-in-glass materials are generally fabricated into rods and their ends finished to high optical tolerances. Both are room-temperature lasers, with Nd-in-glass being 2 to 3 times more efficient and less sensitive to temperature changes than ruby. Ruby was the first laser material and it is still the most mechanically durable.

Since both ruby and Nd-in-glass laser materials are electrically insulating, they must be powered by a means other than simple electrical excitation. The method used to inject energy into the materials is to generate a very intense light flux which can be absorbed by the laser material and converted into a collimated laser beam. The pump used to optically excite the laser material is usually an arc-discharge lamp.

To efficiently use the light produced by the lamp, the laser rod and lamp are usually placed in an optical cavity. Such a structure may be in the form of an elliptical or circular cylinder to focus the light from a linear arc-discharge lamp onto the laser rod, as shown in Fig. 6-15. Ruby and Nd-in-glass are usually operated in a pulsed manner using xenon filled flashlamps.

The energy source for the pulsed flashlamps usually consists of a DC power supply and a bank of energy storage capacitors. The capacitors are charged to a predetermined voltage and their stored energy is then discharged through an inductor to limit current peaks, and then through the flashlamp to create the necessary pump light.

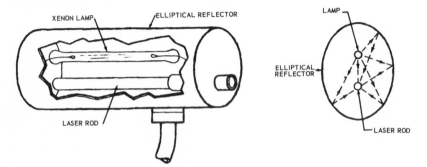

**Fig. 6–15.**   Elliptical focusing structure using linear lamp.

The conversion efficiency from electrical energy to laser light energy is about .5 to 5 per cent; thus, industrial laser systems generally require cooling to maintain reasonable temperatures inside the laser head. Air streams are used to cool low-duty-cycle equipment, while closed-cycle refrigerated water systems are most generally used for high average power equipment.

Pulsed laser systems require maintenance, of course. The majority of the system is conventional electronic and cooling equipment which requires very little maintenance. The laser head has only one component, the flashlamp, which requires frequent replacement. The flashlamp life is largely dependent on the energy input to it, and the current pulse shape. Flashlamp life can vary from as short as a few hundred shots in a piece of research equipment, to about one-half million shots in a conservatively designed piece of industrial equipment. In general, pulsed laser systems currently on the market have been designed to provide a flashlamp life of between 10,000 and 100,000 operations between lamp replacements.

### Process Description

A typical laser system can have an output energy of 20 joules with a pulse duration of $10^{-3}$ sec., corresponding to a peak power of 20,000 w. A typical beam divergence for such a laser is approximately $2 \times 10^{-3}$ radians. If a 1.0 in. focal length lens is used to focus this energy, the spot diameter exposed to the focused laser beam becomes $2 \times 10^{-3}$ in., or an area of approximately $3 \times 10^{-6}$ in². A power of 20,000 w. focused onto an area of $3 \times 10^{-6}$ in² results in a power density of $7 \times 10^9$ w/in² (see Fig. 6-16). A power density of this magnitude is sufficient to vaporize any known metal and even a diamond. Thus, a laser is capable of drilling a hole in any metal.

Not all of the material is removed by evaporation, however; laser machining is basically a high-speed ablation process as illustrated in Fig. 6-16. The evaporation of a very small portion of the liquid metal takes place so rapidly under the high intensities of a focused laser beam that a substantial impulse is transmitted to the liquid. Material leaves the surface not only through evaporation, but also in the liquid state at a relatively high velocity.

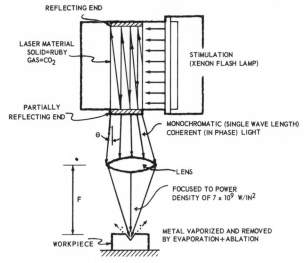

**Fig. 6–16.** The laser machining process.

In machining a hole with a laser beam, a short high-intensity pulse is desirable. The amount of energy needed to raise a volume of material to its vaporization point can be calculated, approximately, as the energy required to raise the metal to its vaporization point plus the latent heat of fusion and vaporization as shown in the computation below.

For example, to drill a hole .45 in. in diameter in a steel sheet .04 in. thick by means of a laser, the volume of the metal to be evaporated equals:

$$6.4 \times 10^{-5} \text{ in}^3 \cong (1 \text{ mm}^3) \text{ or } (.008 \text{ gm.}) \tag{2}$$

The energy required for vaporization of 1.0 gm. of the metal requires:
a) Heating it from room temperature to melting point:

$$E_1 = C (T_m - T_o) = .11 (1535 - 20) = 167 \text{ cal.} \tag{3}$$

b) Changing it from solid to liquid at $T_m$:

$$E_2 = L_f = 65 \text{ cal.} \tag{4}$$

c) Heating it from melting point to boiling point:

$$E_3 = C(T_b - T_m) = .11 (3000 - 1535) = 161 \text{ cal.} \tag{5}$$

d) Changing it from liquid to vapor at $T_b$:

$$E_4 = L_v = 1630 \text{ cal.} \tag{6}$$

$$\text{and } E_1 + E_2 + E_3 + E_4 = 2023 \text{ cal.} = 8500 \text{ joules} \tag{7}$$

Where:   $C$   = Specific heat in cal/gm

   $T_0$   = Ambient temperature in °C.

   $T_m$   = Melting temperature in °C.

   $T_b$   = Boiling temperature in °C.

   $L_f$   = Heat of fusion in cal/gm

   $L_v$   = Heat of vaporization in cal/gm

Thus, vaporization of .008 gm. (1.0 mm³) of the metal requires approximately 68 joules.

Assuming that it requires a laser energy on the order of 100 joules and assuming, also, a pulse length of $10^{-5}$ sec., the required power would be:

$$\frac{10^2 \text{ joules}}{10^{-5} \text{ sec.}} = 10^7 \text{ w.} \tag{8}$$

If the laser beam is properly controlled so as to permit melting, but not vaporization and expulsion, it can be used for welding. Unlike conventional welding, pulse duration is not a critical factor for laser machining. However, a long pulse produces a larger heat-affected zone and a large amount of molten metal surrounding the hole. To obtain uniformity in the laser machined hole, it is necessary to maintain a uniform energy density over the area to be drilled during the laser pulse. The area over which the energy is applied is usually controlled with simple optical techniques.

The power intensity of laser beams must be carefully controlled in order to obtain a desired result. If the intensity is increased sufficiently high and the pulse duration is short, vaporization on the metal surface occurs and vaporized metal is thrown off from the surface.

To meet the basic requirements for industrial applications, the laser systems must meet the following specifications: (1) sufficient power output, (2) controlled pulse length, (3) suitable focusing system, (4) adequate repetition rate, (5) reliability of operation, and (6) suitable safety characteristics. Although laser systems have improved steadily in design and performance, further advances in efficiency, repetition rate, laser material, pumping systems, cooling systems, optical systems, etc., are still needed in order for LBM to be adapted as an industrial tool for wide application.

### Economic Considerations

One of the present drawbacks in laser applications is cost. Any industrial application of the laser should be based on one of two criteria: (1) it can perform a superior job in terms of quality and cost over existing methods, or (2) it is the only tool capable or available for the specific job. The cost of using laser systems falls into 2 categories: (1) the capital investment for the laser system, and (2) the operational cost. At the present time, both the equipment and direct operational costs of a laser are higher than those of comparable conventional equipment and methods.

The operating cost for the laser includes replacement and maintenance costs for flashlamps, capacitors, ruby rods, optics, power, and labor. A typical example (1) of the operational cost breakdown is:

| | |
|---|---|
| Flashlamp (10,000 shots/lamp) | 2.0 ¢ /shot |
| Other maintenance | .2 ¢ |
| Labor and overhead | .5 ¢ |
| Utilities | .01 ¢ |
| Depreciation | .2 ~ 2 ¢ |
| Total | 2.9 ~ 4.7 ¢ /shot |

The major operational cost of a laser system is the replacement cost of flashlamps. In general, the average cost of laser operation is 2 to 3 cents per laser shot.

## Advantages and Limitations

Because of the laser's ability to machine through optically transparent materials, melt or vaporize any known metal, and operate in any desired atmospheric environment, it is preferred over EBM in many applications. In addition to high cost, the process has several limitations, however. The advantages and limitations of laser machining are summarized in Table VI-6.

### Table VI-6. Advantages and Limitations of Laser Machining

*Advantages*

1) No direct contact between tool (laser) and workpiece
2) Will machine and weld through optically transparent materials
3) Welding and machining of areas not readily accessible
4) Will melt or vaporize any known material
5) Easily weld dissimilar materials
6) Refractory metals are easy to work with
7) Machining of brittle, non-metallic, hard materials
8) Welding and machining in any desired atmospheric environment
9) Small heat affected zones, and negligible thermal damage or effect on adjacent regions
10) Machining extremely small holes and precision welding of small sizes
11) Easy control of beam configuration and size of exposed area

*Limitations*

1) Overall efficiency is low
2) Pulsed mode operation (solid state)
3) Practically limited to thin sheet plate or wire fabrication
4) Holes machined not always round nor straight
5) Control of hole size and weldage size is difficult
6) Repetition rate is slow
7) Durability and reliability are limited
8) Short life of flashlamp
9) Necessity for careful control of pulse length and power intensity to obtain a desired effect
10) Effective safety procedures required
11) High cost

## Applications

Optically pumped lasers have been used for a large variety of hole drilling applications. In general, the laser can be used most economically when the volume of material to be removed is small. Typically, the laser can be used to remove material when the hole diameter required is less than approximately .125 in. and the material is not more than .5 in. thick. This is not to say that the laser cannot be used for applications outside of this range, but more careful cost evaluation would be required for the larger volume applications. The laser is also useful for removing not only cylindrical sections, but conical and rectangular sections as well.

## Drilling Holes

Fig. 6-17 shows a matrix of laser drilled holes. The 10 by 10 hole matrix was drilled in a .078 in. thick wall of zirconia tube. Approximately 10, 3-joule pulses

**Fig. 6-17.** Zirconia tube with matrix of laser drilled holes. *(Courtesy, Westinghouse Electric Research and Development Center)*

of energy, each .5 msec. in duration, were used to produce the .005 in. diameter holes. The laser was used only after USM, AJM, and EBM techniques had been tried. These attempts failed because they either could not hold the hole tolerance or else the material cracked so that it later failed. This zirconia tube with its matrix of holes has been temperature-cycled to over 1000°C. many times without cracking.

Small diameter holes through materials such as cast iron are frequently required. The use of fine wire drills can be expensive since they are easily broken and cause the workpiece to be scrapped. On one job, a hole was required in a cast iron assembly to permit the flow of a specified volume of air. The casting was .210 in. thick. Fig. 6-18 shows the cross-section of the hole that resulted when a 146 joule, 5 msec. pulse of laser energy was brought to focus on the

**Fig. 6-18.** Cast iron, .210 in. thick, laser drilled. *(Courtesy, Westinghouse Electric Research and Development Center)*

workpiece. Multiple laser pulses could be used to improve the uniformity of the hole cross-section, but the application only required a flow specification.

Fig. 6-19 shows the top surface of .060 in. thick piece of tungsten carbide with 2 laser drilled holes. Each hole is conical, with a .040 in. diameter on top and .010 in. diameter on the back side. Four 50-joule, 1.0 msec. long laser pulses were used to drill these holes. Fewer pulses would have resulted in

**Fig. 6–19.** Top surface of .060 in. thick piece of tungsten carbide with 2 laser drilled holes. *(Courtesy, Westinghouse Electric Research and Development Center)*

material removal without breakthrough; more pulses would have resulted in a more cylindrical hole. Tungsten carbide is usually machined by diamond grinding, a more costly method than the laser.

Fig. 6-20 shows a hole in .003 in. thick aluminum sheet made by a 2.3 joule burst of a laser beam through a 32 mm. lens, with the workpiece at the focal point. Front (*a*) and rear (*b*) sides of the .015 in. hole are shown. The elliptical circle surrounding the hole indicates the heat-affected zone.

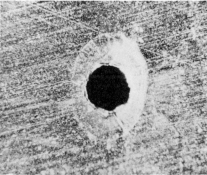

**Fig. 6–20.** Hole in .003 in. thick aluminum sheet made by a 2.3 joule burst of a laser beam through a 32 mm. lens, with the workpiece at the focal point. Hole diameter: .015 in., (a) front side, (b) rear side. Elliptical circle surrounding hole indicates heat-affected zone. 50 magnification. *(Courtesy, Pennsylvania State University)*

Fig. 6-21 shows the front and back surfaces of .003 in. sheet aluminum, 18 per cent Ni maraging steel, and Type 302 stainless steel, laser machined

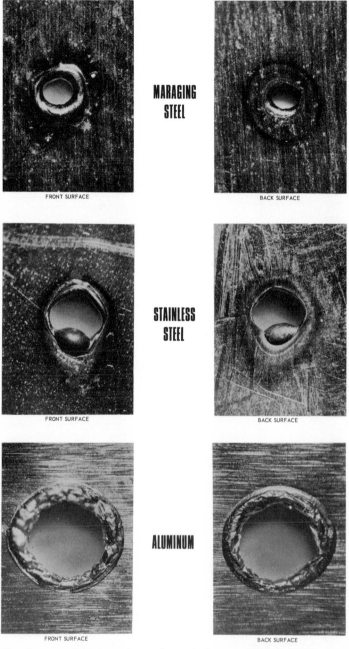

**Fig. 6–21.** Front and back surfaces of metals laser machined. Thickness: .003 in. Energy: 4 joules. 50 magnification. *(Courtesy, Pennsylvania State University)*

with 4 joules. The thicknesses and surfaces of two tandemly-drilled holes in
.062 in. cold rolled steel, using 12 pulses of 4 joules each, is shown in Figs.
6-22 through 6-25. A 12:1 depth-to-width ratio laser drilled hole in .125 in.

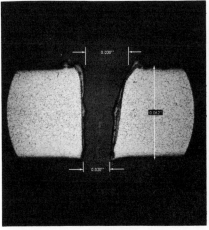

**Fig. 6-22.** First thickness of two .062 in. cold-rolled steel samples drilled in tandem, 12 pulses of 4 joules. Note typical expulsion. *(Courtesy, General Electric Company)*

**Fig. 6-23.** Second thickness of tandem drilling, masked by section shown in Fig. 6-22. *(Courtesy, General Electric Company)*

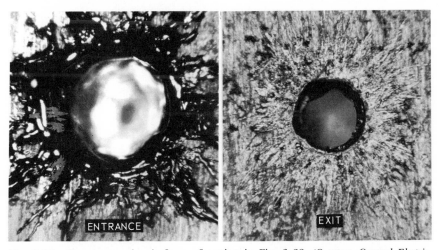

**Fig. 6-24.** Entrance and exit faces of section in Fig. 6-22. *(Courtesy, General Electric Company)*

high carbon steel sheet is shown in Fig. 6-26. To laser machine the .250 in.
presintered alumina in Fig. 6-27, 50 pulses of 5 joules each were used. The
hole shown in Fig. 6-28 was laser drilled at 45 deg. through .062 in. stainless
steel sheet with 4 pulses of 2.2 joules each.

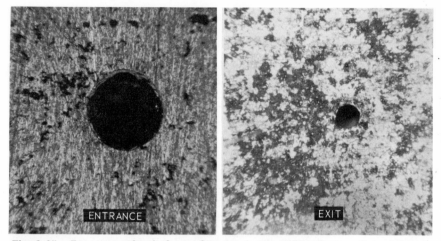

**Fig. 6–25.** Entrance and exit faces of section in Fig. 6–23. *(Courtesy, General Electric Company)*

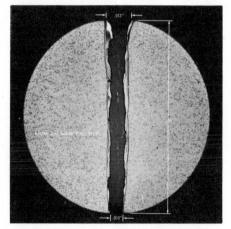

**Fig. 6–26.** Laser-drilled hole in .125 in. high carbon steel sheet, 12:1 depth-to-width ratio. *(Courtesy, General Electric Company)*

### Future Potential

The laser today is a useful machine tool for many applications. While the continuous $CO_2$-$N_2$ gas laser is still a laboratory device, the pulsed laser has been developed into an industrial tool. For large production applications, the cost of operating a pulsed laser system can be as low as .1 cent/operation and potentially lower. Laser systems can be constructed for industrial applications with outputs from fractions of 1.0 joule to more than 1000 joules. Most laser equipment can be designed so that personnel who can be trained to use a microscope and resistance welder can also be taught to use a laser.

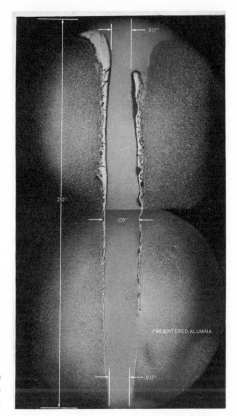

**Fig. 6–27.** Presintered alumina .250 in. thick penetrated by 50 pulses of 5 joules. *(Courtesy, General Electric Company)*

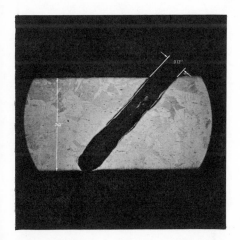

**Fig. 6–28.** Hole laser drilled at 45 deg. through 1/16 in. stainless steel sheet, 4 pulses of 2.2 joules. *(Courtesy, Pennsylvania State University)*

## PLASMA ARC MACHINING

A plasma is defined as a gas which has been heated to a sufficiently high temperature to become partially ionized. Various devices utilizing an electric arc to heat gas to the plasma state have been in existence since the early 1900's. However, the refinement of this apparatus to develop commercial plasma equipment for metal cutting dates back only about 10 years. _1957_ _IN_

Plasma cutting refers to metal cutting of the type accomplished by oxy-fuel torches. Early applications of plasma arc cutting were primarily on difficult-to-cut metals such as stainless steel, Monel, and the super alloys. The operation is normally used for the cutoff or rough shaping of plates or bars and, where the oxygen cutting stream penetrates entirely through the metal thickness, it can be used on a severing operation. It now seems evident that very similar equipment can be effectively used to replace conventional machining operations such as lathe turning, milling and planing.

Since plasma cutting is a relatively common process described in a substantial amount of published data, this section will cover only plasma arc machining (PAM).

### Process Principles

In PAM, the basic plasma is generated by subjecting a volume of gas to the electron bombardment of an electric arc. The high-velocity electrons of the arc collide with the gas molecules and produce dissociation of diatomic molecules followed by ionization of the atoms. Fig. 6-29 shows the DC arc being

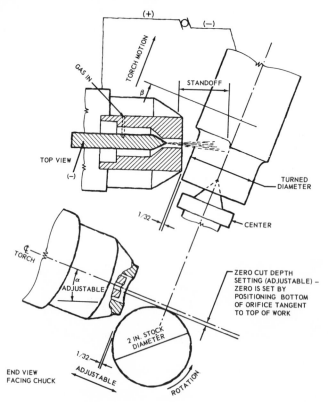

**Fig. 6-29.** Plasma turning; torch to work geometry.

struck from a cathode within the plasma generator to the workpiece (anode) located outside the torch, and the torch to work geometry in plasma turning. The plasma forming gas is forced through the nozzle duct in such a manner as to stabilize the arc. Much of the heating of the gas takes place in the constricted region of the nozzle duct resulting in a relatively high gas exit velocity and a very high core temperature.

The basic heating phenomenon that takes place at the workpiece is a combination of anode heating due to direct electron bombardment, plus convective heating from the high temperature plasma that accompanies the arc. In some cases, it is desirable to achieve a third source of heating by injecting oxygen into the work area and taking advantage of the exothermic oxidation reaction. Once the material has been raised to the molten point, the high-velocity gas stream effectively blows the material away (see Fig. 6-30). For an optimized PAM cutting or machining operation, up to 45 per cent of the electrical power delivered to the torch is used to remove metal from the workpiece.

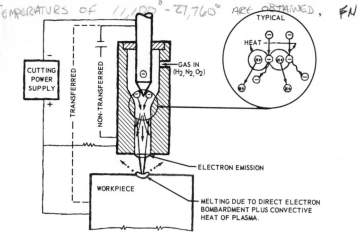

**Fig. 6–30.** Schematic of plasma arc machining.

Of the remaining power, approximately 10 per cent goes into the cooling water in the plasma generator and the rest is wasted in the hot gas and in heating up the workpiece.

As shown in Fig. 6-31, the remaining items of a complete PAM setup include: a motion control for the torch, a rotational device for the workpiece, an exhaust hood for venting the area, plus a control console, DC rectifier power supply, and a supply of appropriate gases for the plasma torch. A cooling water loop is required to maintain proper operating temperature of the plasma generator electrodes.

The variables associated with the PAM operation can be divided into 3 categories: (1) those associated with the operation of the torch, (2) those associated with the physical configuration of the setup, and (3) those associated with the environment in which the work is performed. The influence of these variables is discussed briefly in the following paragraphs but, to be meaningful, the following idealized metal removal concepts should be kept in mind. The

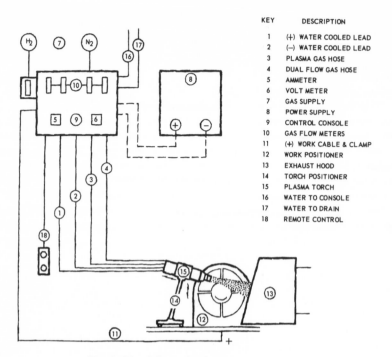

KEY     DESCRIPTION

| | |
|---|---|
| 1 | (+) WATER COOLED LEAD |
| 2 | (−) WATER COOLED LEAD |
| 3 | PLASMA GAS HOSE |
| 4 | DUAL FLOW GAS HOSE |
| 5 | AMMETER |
| 6 | VOLT METER |
| 7 | GAS SUPPLY |
| 8 | POWER SUPPLY |
| 9 | CONTROL CONSOLE |
| 10 | GAS FLOW METERS |
| 11 | (+) WORK CABLE & CLAMP |
| 12 | WORK POSITIONER |
| 13 | EXHAUST HOOD |
| 14 | TORCH POSITIONER |
| 15 | PLASMA TORCH |
| 16 | WATER TO CONSOLE |
| 17 | WATER TO DRAIN |
| 18 | REMOTE CONTROL |

**Fig. 6-31.** Schematic of PAM apparatus.

production of an acceptably smooth surface with high metal removal rate by PAM requires efficient coupling of the sources of heat to the workpiece with minimum heat transfer to the remaining material. The flow of the molten material being removed must be in such a direction that it does not tend to adhere to the hot surface that has just been machined.

**Torch.** The torch variables include: the electrical power delivered, the gases used to form the plasma, the flow rate of the gases through the torch, the orifice diameter through the nozzle duct, and any possible secondary gas streams. In general, there is an optimum exit orifice size for operation at a particular power level which will produce a well-controlled high-velocity plasma jet with maximized capacity for performing the material removal operation. Thus, gas flow rate, orifice size, and power level are intimately related. This relationship has been well established for existing PAM equipment.

The principal remaining variable is the selection of gases for the process. Since the standard cathode material is thoriated tungsten, the plasma gas normally does not include any oxygen. It has been determined that a mixture of nitrogen plus 20 per cent hydrogen provides maximum removal rates for some non-ferrous metals. The relationship between nozzle orifice area and metal removal rate for various gas combinations is illustrated in Fig. 6-32. The curves show that removal rate rises to a peak and then decreases as nozzle size is increased. Power, speed, feed, gas flow and turning geometry are held constant. The tendency of hydrogen to recombine on a surface, thereby transferring its energy of recombination to the surface, explains the significant advantage in the use of hydrogen in the process. Little work has been done to date in optimizing the injection of oxygen into the plasma for ferrous metal machining, but significant improvements have been made in PAM by including oxygen.

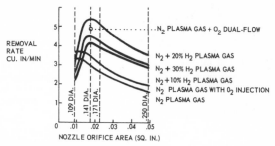

Fig. 6–32. Removal rate as a function of nozzle size for various plasma gases. Power, speed, feed, gas flow, turning geometry are constants.

**Physical Configuration.** In the physical orientation of PAM operations, such variables as torch standoff, angle to the work, depth of cut, feed into the work, and speed of the work toward the torch are involved. The feed and depth of cut determine the volume of metal removed. Removal rate as a function of torch angle $\beta$ is illustrated in Fig. 6-33. As shown by the curve, as $\beta$ increases, the metal removal rate increases to a maximum and then decreases.

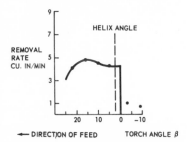

Fig. 6–33. Removal rate as a function of torch angle $\beta$. Constants: plasma gas $N_2 + 20$ per cent $H_2$, .141 diameter nozzle, speed and feed.

The increase of removal rate to the peak takes place because of better purging of the molten products from the work surface. The decrease of removal rate after the peak is caused by an increase in the arc standoff distance which permits greater convective and radiant heat losses, lower jet impingement velocity, and less metal melting. When operating at the 50 kw. power level, the maximum practical depth of cut is in the range of .250 to .375 in. For 2 in. diameter workpieces, the feed of the torch into the work can be up to approximately .250 in. if the resulting cusps or helical grooves can be tolerated. To produce a smooth surface, however, the maximum feed is approximately .031 in.

Fig. 6-34 shows a typical PAM bar turning operation with the workpiece supported in a lathe and the torch supported by a variable-speed drive mechanism. The angle of the torch is pointed ahead in the direction of torch motion so that the molten material is blown off over the cool unmachined surface.

The overall relationship of spindle speed, feed, and removal rate can be seen in the 3-dimensional graph in Fig. 6-35.

**Fig. 6–34.** Turning a 2 in. diameter steel bar. Torch is moving to left as bar rotates. *(Courtesy, Thermal Dynamics Corporation)*

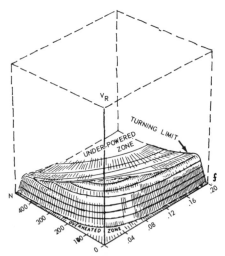

**Fig. 6–35.** A three-dimensional graph showing spindle speed as a function of feed for various metal removal rates.

**Work Environment.** The environmental group of variables for PAM includes any cooling that is done on the bar, any protective type of atmosphere used to reduce oxidation of the exposed high temperature machined surface, and any means that might be utilized to spread out or deflect the arc and plasma impingement area. In general, very little has been done to investigate the effects of these various techniques for improving the operation, although it is commonly accepted that significant advancements can be made in the process by optimizing these various areas.

### Typical PAM Results

The graph in Fig. 6-36 shows the interrelationships among some of the factors involved in plasma arc turning. Since the torch carriage speed and direction are not coupled to the work spindle as they might be on an ordinary lathe, it is necessary to calculate the carriage speed in order to produce a turned piece with a predetermined pitch (pitch = feed). The graph allows this to be accomplished easily, at the same time outlining areas of desirable operations.

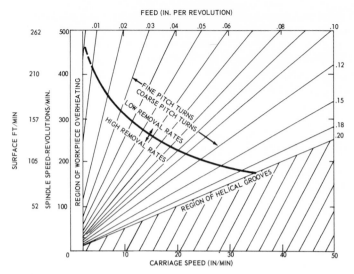

**Fig. 6-36.** 50 kw speed-feed graph for 2 in. diameter carbon steel.

When operating at the 50 kw. level on 2 in. diameter rods, the maximum removal rate for satisfactory surface finish is approximately 7 cu. in/min. As illustrated in Fig. 6-37, the surface finish can vary anywhere from helical ridges along the surface to a completely smooth surface with approximately 30 microinch rms. finish, depending on the feed into the work and optimization of the process. PAM operation for maximum removal rate does produce a slight helical ridge as the cut progresses.

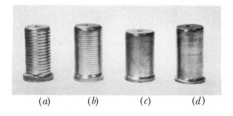

**Fig. 6-37.** 2 in. diameter carbon steel specimens turned at feed rates of: (a) .187 in., (b) .120 in., (c) .060 in., and (d) .030 in. (Courtesy, Thermal Dynamics Corporation)

(a)    (b)    (c)    (d)

One characteristic of the surface when operating without workpiece cooling is a gradual inward taper in the direction of the cut. This is believed to be due to accumulated heating of the workpiece as the cut progresses and should be minimized or eliminated by appropriate cooling methods. An oxidation scale normally forms behind the cut on an unprotected specimen, but this can be minimized or eliminated by proper shielding.

## Metallurgical Effects

The metallurgical effects of the PAM process are as widely varied as the materials used and their respective metallurgical histories. As previously described, the PAM process inherently involves heating the surface material to the molten point and then allowing it to cool either gradually or rapidly, depending on the auxiliary equipment used. In general, the depth of the heat affected zone is approximately .030 in. For some operations, this hardened material would have to be removed, although for other applications, such a hardened surface may be desirable. The nature of individual applications of the PAM process would have to determine the metallurgical effects that could be tolerated.

## Economic Considerations

An approximation of the cost/hr of the PAM process using the removal rate of 7 cu. in/min could be derived as follows:

| | |
|---|---:|
| Power = 50 kw. at 2.5 ¢/kw | $1.25 |
| Plasma gas: | |
| Nitrogen, 35 SCFH at 1.5 ¢/cu. ft. | .53 |
| Hydrogen, 10 SCFH at 1.5 ¢/cu. ft. | .15 |
| Labor ($3.50/hr.); overhead (100 per cent) | 7.00 |
| Electrode replacements | .62 |
| | $9.55 |

Metal removed per hour = 420 cu. in. or 119 lbs.
Cost per cu. in. of metal removed = $.023
Cost per lb. of metal removed = $.080

## Advantages and Limitations

The principal advantages of the PAM process are that it is almost equally effective on any metal regardless of hardness or refractory nature, plus the fact that it provides mechanical decoupling of the tool and the workpiece so that only simple support structures are required. The principal disadvantages are the metallurgical alteration of the surface and the characteristic of the surface profile produced. These disadvantages may lead to the requirement for a subsequent secondary machining operation to remove up to .050 in. unless the application can tolerate the hardened or uneven surface.

## Future Potential

Some of the applications for which the PAM process is being considered include the turning of rolls for structural shape rolling mills, pulley grooving, and turning large shafts of hardened and low machinability material. In order for the process to be used in any of these applications, however, the process characteristics which make it usable now as a rough turning tool for moderate sized barstock must be understood much more completely before it can be used for more sophisticated applications.

## ION BEAM MACHINING

### Operating Principle

Although ion beam machining (IBM) is included with the thermo-electric processes, it does not rely primarily on heating the workpiece locally to the evaporation temperature. Therefore, this process differs fundamentally from electron beam or laser machining.

Ion beam machining depends on sputtering. In this process, a bombarding ion will dislodge surface atoms by the transfer of kinetic energy from the incident ion much in the same manner that a cue ball striking a packed mass of other billiard balls will scatter one or more of them away from the group. This analogy can be somewhat more accurate if it is imagined that the group of billiard balls is held together by a very weak elastic adhesive at the points of contact, representing the interatomic "binding energy" that holds solid materials together.

The sputtering coefficient—the number of atoms or molecules dislodged for each ingoing ion—is a statistical process dependent upon the energy and atomic weight of the ingoing ion, the angle of incidence, and the physical and chemical nature of the bombarded piece. As a general rule, the sputtering coefficient increases with the atomic weight of the bombarding ion and with the angle of incidence, grazing incidence giving the highest yield. The sputtering yield at first increases with the kinetic energy of the bombarding atom, but later falls off. This is because highly energetic ions penetrate the bombarded material and share more of their energy with the internal, rather than the surface, atoms. The effect of these various parameters is shown in Fig. 6-38 for the specific examples of vitreous silica (3, 4).

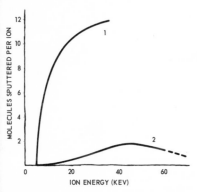

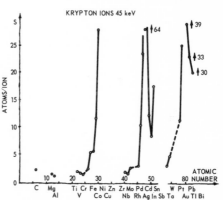

**Fig. 6–38.** Sputtering yields of vitreous silica for *(1)* argon ions at 60° incidence *(2)* xenon ions at 0° (normal) incidence.

**Fig. 6–39.** Sputtering ratios of Kr ions on different materials. Xe sputtering is somewhat higher than that of Kr and has the same periodicity (8).

The dependence on the bombarded material is complex (see Fig. 6-39) for the elements for one specific bombarding particle and energy.

## Applications

There are two ways of applying the sputtering process. Currently, it is used for the deposition of films, particularly in the electronics industry. In typical apparatus, the material to be deposited is made the anode in a low pressure argon or other rare gas atmosphere. Gaseous ions bombard the cathode, sputtering its material on the substrate. Since IBM is not a true machining process, further discussion of applications is not warranted. The use of IBM to provide selective removal of material has yet to find commercial application. However, some suggested uses have been made.

Hines and Wallor demonstrated the removal of vitreous silica by the sputtering technique in 1961 (3) and this has been further examined by Bashkin, *et al.* (5, 6) as a method of figuring optical surfaces. An attractive feature of the method is the possibility of continuous interferametric examination of the surfaces while it is being machined. One disadvantage of the technique would seem to be the heating and consequent local distortion of the surface. Since this particular application does not require high resolution machining, except in depth, the deposition sputtering approach may be preferable.

The real potential value of the IBM technique lies in micromachining. In principle, ion beam equipment can be designed having greater resolution than equivalent energy electron beam equipment. This is exemplified in the field ion microscope where individual atoms of a crystal surface can be displayed. The electron microscope has less resolution power.

The technique of micromachining is likely to find application in microcircuits and other semiconductor electronics. Castaigne, *et al.*, have shown (7) that patterns may be machined into surfaces with line widths of .2 micrometer (8 mm. in.). The apparatus used is illustrated in Fig. 6-40. A master mask is illuminated by the energetic ion beam and projected by an electrostatic lens onto

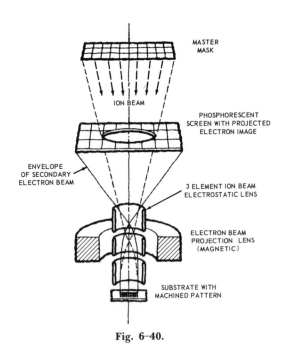

Fig. 6-40.

the substrate to be machined. Reduction factors of 50 or more are readily achievable. In the example, a wire grid is projected onto the substrate. A novel method of displaying the pattern being machined consists of back projecting the secondary electrons on to a phosphorescent screen that can be directly observed. The magnetic projection lens has no significant effect on the ion beam.

## Limitations

Fundamental limitations of IBM are imposed by the relatively high capital costs of equipments and the extremely small amount of material that is removed. Removal rates of a few thousandths of an inch per hour for the micromachinery applications are the best that can be predicted for the present state-of-the-art. This is in principle economically adequate for figuring optical surfaces, microcircuit machinery and, perhaps, for the precision fabrication of fine wire dies in refractory materials.

### REFERENCES

1. J. E. Jackson, "Pulsed Laser Welding," Research Report, Linde Division, Union Carbide Corporation, Indianapolis, Indiana (September, 1964).
2. "Plasma Arc Machining," Report No. AMRA CR66-03/F submitted to U.S. Army Materials Research Agency.
3. Hines, R. L. and R. Wallor, *Journal of Applied Physics, 32* (1961) 202.
4. Nablo, S. V. and W. J. King, "High Vacuum Sputtering of Electronic Materials," Paper No. 64–484 presented at National Electronic Conference, Chicago, Illinois, October, 1964.
5. Meinel, A. B., S. Bashkin, and D. A. Loomis, *Applied Optics 4* (1965) 1674.
6. Schroeder, J. B., S. Bashkin, and J. F. Nester, *Applied Optics 5* (1966) 1031.
7. Castaigne, J., "Ion Beam Machinery," post deadline paper, Second International Conference on Electron and Ion Beam Science and Technology, New York, New York, July, 1966.
8. O. Almen, *et al., Collection and Sputtering Experiments with Noble Gas Ions—Electroncynetic Separation of Radioactive Isotopes* (Vienna, Austria: Springer-Verlag, 1961).

# INDEX

171